EVOLUTION AND RELIGION

The Conflict Between Science and Religion in Modern America

Problems in American Civilization

UNDER THE EDITORIAL DIRECTION OF

George Rogers Taylor

EVOLUTION AND RELIGION

The Conflict Between Science and Theology in Modern America

EDITED WITH AN INTRODUCTION BY

Gail Kennedy

Problems in American Civilization

READINGS SELECTED BY THE
DEPARTMENT OF AMERICAN STUDIES
AMHERST COLLEGE

D. C. HEATH AND COMPANY: Boston

INTRODUCTION

TRADITIONALLY the history of the Western world has been divided, like ancient Gaul, into three parts, but the more significant division is into what precedes the scientific revolution of the sixteenth century and everything that has occurred since. For the events of the latter period are unique. What makes them so is the advent of modern science. Modern science has reoriented men's thinking about the nature of the world in which they live and through its technological fruits has transformed their institutions. The whole of modern times has been one vast slow revolution, a revolution still proceeding. This intellectual and cultural revolution has passed through five main phases as one area of experience after another has been yielded, reluctantly, as a proper field of scientific inquiry. The phases of this revolution may be associated with certain representative names: (1) Space—Copernicus, "On the Revolutions of the Heavenly Bodies" (1543); (2) Time—Lyell, "The Principles of Geology" (1830–32); (3) Life—Darwin, "The Origin of Species" (1859); (4) Society—Marx, "Capital" (1867); (5) Mind—Freud, "The Interpretation of Dreams" (1900); (6) Method—Einstein, "The Special Theory of Relativity" (1905).

Note the accelerating pace of this development. And observe that this gradual conquest begins with what is most *remote* from men's inclinations and desires, mathematics, astronomy, and physics. This first period of the expansion of science culminates in the synthesis made by Newton at the end of the seventeenth century. But it is not until the nineteenth century that a real beginning is made in the historical sciences—those for which *time* is the focal concept—of geology, biology, and sociology by men such as Lyell, Darwin, and Marx. Finally, the innermost citadel of resistance to the application of scientific method, the *human personality* itself, is attacked by Freud; and the last pretence that we can know reality as it is in itself, the very quest for certainty, is *abandoned in principle* with the general acceptance of Einstein's theory of relativity. The outlines of science as a human construction may therefore now be said to be complete.

The result of this immense shift in the climate of opinion, together with the cumulative effect of technology, has been to engraft upon the historical process a new dimension. Modern science and technology have imposed a radically different kind of organization upon our lives, making our pattern of culture—one in which "atomic" and "automation" are ordinary words—entirely foreign to anything ever before seen in the world.

Of the successive phases in this advance the extension of scientific inquiry into the biological realm was the most difficult to accept. Newtonian science had been thoroughly assimilated to traditional beliefs by the construction of a system of natural theology in which it was affirmed that all physical events happen in accordance with *rational laws* and have, when properly understood, a *use*. Therefore, the progress of scientific knowledge revealed more and more details of a cosmic plan. The world described by the scientists was a second revelation expressed not in words but in events occurring in space and time. The favorite illustrations of this organization of the world by an intelligent power were drawn from the field of biology. How, for example, could such marvellous instances of adaptation as the hand or the eye have originated unless they were deliberately made to serve their purpose? Thus the facts of biological adaptation were used as "evidences" for religion, and the religious motive fostered a belief in the creation of fixed species.

The impact of the theory of evolution upon this system of natural theology came in three successive waves, each initiated by the publication of a book: Lyell's *Principles* (1830–32), Darwin's *Origin* (1859) and Darwin's *The Descent of Man* (1871). During the first stage of the controversy the problem was to reconcile *Genesis* with geology. At the time Lyell's book appeared the prevailing theory was that of the "Catastrophists." Their view was that in a number of successive epochs in the past, the last of which was the age of Noah, great cataclysms had taken place. After each of these catastrophes new species were created to people the earth. Only in this way was it possible to explain the geological record in a world that was created, according to the calculation of Bishop Ussher, in the year 4004 B.C. In opposition to this conception of geological processes there was the "Uniformitarian" hypothesis, "that *no causes whatever* have from the earliest time to which we can look back to the present, ever acted, but those that are *now acting*, and that they never acted with different degrees of energy from that which they now exert." This hypothesis, as it had been advanced in the late eighteenth century by James Hutton, was generally ignored. By Lyell, however, who developed it independently, it was applied with such powerful reasoning and copiousness of detail that it had to be accepted. Since Lyell's hypothesis required enormous periods of time for the slow forces of erosion, deposition, compression, etc. to do their work the conflict between geology and *Genesis*, which already existed, became acute. In America such distinguished scientists as Benjamin Silliman and his pupil Edward Hitchcock endeavored to resolve the ap-

parent contradiction. In 1851 Hitchcock, then president of Amherst College, published a book, *The Religion of Geology*, which provided a definitive rehabilitation of natural theology. "The principles of science," said Hitchcock, "are a transcript of the Divine Character." It follows that there can be no real inconsistency between science and scripture; on the contrary, they must complement one another. By analyzing the Hebrew word for "day" he concluded that it was an indefinite term which could be used to denote any period. And, since the main purpose of the Bible is a moral one, it is not surprising that phenomena are described with no particular attempt at scientific precision. With great ingenuity Hitchcock then proceeds to apply the results of geological science to an interpretation of the Mosaic account of creation and he is able to show that geology is not merely consistent with the Scriptures but positively reinforces our belief in them.

This revision of natural theology had just been completed when Darwin's *Origin of Species* appeared. Upon this reinforcement of religion by science Darwin's extension of the uniformitarian hypothesis to the field of biology was a direct attack. For Darwin's hypothesis of the gradual transformation of species rested upon two presumptions: (1) that minute spontaneous variations are constantly occurring in all individual organisms and that these variations are inheritable; (2) that there is a dual process of incessant competition between the individual organisms comprising a given species and also of these species groups with other rival or enemy groups. As a consequence of these two factors some individuals within a species group, and also each species group as a whole will be at an advantage or disadvantage in the struggle for survival; and, over a very long period of time, through this process of natural selection, gradual transformations of species will occur. Evolution as Darwin attempts to explain it depends upon the interaction of two independent variables, inheritable variations and the stresses of the environment.

To say, however, that an event occurs as the consequence of two independent sets of causes is to say that it occurs by *chance*. Thus, in throwing a coin the set of causes which result in the turning up of "heads" has nothing to do (presumably) with the set of causes which result in the placing of a bet. Or, when a stone, loosened by rain, rolls down a steep cut and into the path of an approaching automobile, since the set of causes which resulted in the fall of the stone and that which resulted in the presence of the automobile are independent, we call the collision an "accident." In effect, Darwin's hypothesis stated that there is a gradual transformation of species and that this transformation is effected by an enormous number of minute accidents. The wonderful adaptations of organisms to their environments are not designed, they are results of chance. In view of the existing climate of opinion when it appeared, it is not surprising that this hypothesis was generally considered implausible and repulsive.

Yet the full implications of Darwinism did not become immediately apparent. Of course, many theologians and a few scientists rejected the hypothesis outright as "the latest form of scientific infidelity." But there were others who found a *via media* by accepting evolution up to a point—the exception of man himself who must have been specially created; and there were those who, like the botanist, Asa Gray, tried to reconcile Darwinism with a cosmic purpose by contending that the apparent incompatibility was due to an unnecessary association of the idea of design with that of special creation. Why could not a creator work *through* the evolutionary process, his providence operating, as it were, on the installment plan?

But these conciliatory positions evaded the major point. That Darwin's version of the evolutionary process might be interpreted as the manifestation of some creative power left the real question unanswered. The real question was what is the bearing of his hypothesis upon the belief in the supremacy of man. Was it consistent with the traditional conception of man's place in nature? Could one accept Darwinism and still maintain that man is the be-all and end-all of the evolutionary process? The publication of *The Descent of Man* (1871) brought this basic issue squarely into the foreground. If man is himself a product of evolution, then he is only one species of animal among others who may eventually be surpassed, and is, in any case, like all the others, doomed to eventual extinction. The dilemma seemed unavoidable: if Darwinism is true, then natural theology is doomed.

It was another Englishman, Herbert Spencer, who enabled many people to evade this dilemma. Spencer, starting from a background of physics rather than biology and with an interest primarily in social questions, had formulated independently his own theory of evolution. He first enunciated it two years before the appearance of the *Origin* in an essay which bore the significant title, "Progress, Its Laws and Cause." The equivalent in Spencer's theory of Darwin's "natural selection" was "survival of the fittest." Taken in one sense Spencer's phrase is a tautology, it merely means that whatever is fittest to survive (in a given environment) will do so; but taken in another it is a magic formula which unites to the idea of evolution that of progress. Thus the sting is drawn from Darwin's conception of the evolutionary process as an effect of blind chance. The optimism of Pope's *Essay on Man* can be recovered:

All nature is but art unknown to thee:
All chance, direction which thou canst not see;
All discord, harmony not understood;
All partial evil, universal good;
And, spite of pride, in erring reason's spite,
One truth is clear, *Whatever is, is right.*

Only one modification is needed. The last line should be changed to read "Whatever is, is coming out all right."

Spencer attempted to apply his theory on a vast scale to every field of human inquiry, to construct a system, as he called it, of *Synthetic Philosophy* in which the principle that held the whole together was his theory of evolution. While he himself maintained an agnostic attitude toward traditional religions, John Fiske, his leading disciple in America, endeavored to prove that this version of the doctrine of evolution "shows us distinctly, for the first time, how the creation and perfection of man is the goal toward which nature's work has been tending from the first." Thus Fiske reinstates man in his position as head of the universe. Once more natural theology, though it was no longer a natural theology consonant with the literal interpretation of Scripture, had been restored. But then, Spencer's evolutionary philosophy as a vindication of faith in perpetual and universal progress, could itself be an alternative of a sort for traditional religion.

The vogue of Spencer's writings in America was immense, not merely because he afforded a basis for reconciling evolution with religion but also because he contended that the mainspring of progress in the social sphere was free competition. It is "rugged individualism," whether in a state of nature or within society that ensures the survival of the fittest. America was the country in which economic liberalism had the freest reign and this liberalism was reinforced by the influence upon habits of thought of the frontier where natural selection as a social process was illustrated upon a grand scale. Moreover, Americans were rapidly becoming secularized. As a people preoccupied with the building up of an immense industrial system, they were increasingly imbued with the spirit of modern technology. The old theological beliefs were degenerating into a genteel tradition. Evangelical religion thus lost its basis in American life and it was Spencer's philosophy of individualism and progress which "laid out the broad highway over which American thought travelled in the later years of the century."

While this was the trend of opinion within the dominant groups of American society, it was not true for everyone. There were large numbers of people, especially in the rural and more "backward" areas whose beliefs and habits had been almost entirely unaffected by this intellectual and cultural upheaval. As industrialization gathered momentum the cultural gaps between different sections and classes within the country widened. Such people as the hill folk of Tennessee were still living in essentially the same world, with the same faith and the same way of life, as their pioneer ancestors. Almost literally one could, by travelling a few miles from those shut-in valleys to great cities such as St. Louis or Chicago, move in time from the seventeenth century to the nineteenth. Throughout the latter half of the nineteenth century and for the first decade of the twentieth these "fundamentalists" were fighting a holding action and were in retreat. Then, for reasons which no historian has, as yet, satisfactorily explained, they took to the offensive. As an organized movement Fundamentalism may be said to have started with a set of twelve pamphlets entitled *The Fundamentals: A Testimony*, published during the years 1909–1912. Financed by two wealthy laymen, the pamphlets were to be sent free to "every pastor, evangelist, missionary, theological student, Sunday School superintendent, Y.M.C.A. and Y.W.C.A. secretary in the English speaking world." Eventually some three million copies were so distributed. The five fundamentals testified to in these volumes were: the inerrancy of the Bible, the virgin birth, the atonement, the resurrection and the second coming of Christ. But it was not until 1916 that the World's Christian Fundamentals Association, precursor of many similar organizations, was founded; nor was it until William Jennings Bryan entered the conflict in 1920 that the movement became one of national importance.

This, be it remembered, was the period of "the return to normalcy"; and for a great multitude the word normalcy seemed equivalent to intolerance and reaction. National feeling, raised to a fever pitch during the war, became a virulent brand of "Americanism" in the Ku Klux Klan, with which some of the fundamentalists were associated. At the height of its growth it boasted some six million members. And it was the period when the gangsterism and contempt of law spawned by prohibition made it apparent to many that the country was going to ruin. What was the root of the evil? It was materialism. And who was the parent of that? It was science. So we find the fundamentalists struggling within every Protestant denomination to oust the "modernists" from their positions of power and introducing into twenty state legislatures between 1921 and 1929 some thirty-seven anti-evolution bills.[1] Of these the first to pass was the law in Tennessee. Similar legislation was enacted later in Mississippi and Arkansas and such laws failed of enactment by narrow margins in a number of other states. Informal restrictions through the censorship of textbooks by superintendents of education, local school boards, etc. were widely applied.

The climax of the fundamentalist movement was the trial during the summer of 1925 of John Scopes, a high school teacher in Dayton, Tennessee for violation of the statute prohibiting the teaching of evolution in tax-supported schools. The legal issue in this trial was the validity of a law which threatened to open a breach in our constitutional wall of separation between church and state. But the legal issue was hopelessly obscured by the circumstances under which the trial was held and the characters of the two protagonists, William Jennings Bryan, last of the great leaders of

agrarian democracy, and Clarence Darrow, famous criminal lawyer and a militant agnostic. The trial aroused not merely nationwide but international attention and was accompanied by an immense amount of publicity and bally-hoo. It is estimated that the average daily press file was 165,000 words. Bryan had declared before the Progressive Club of Dayton that "the contest between evolution and Christianity is a duel to the death"; and shortly after the two champions entered the arena the subject of the trial became not an argument over the legal point but science vs. the Bible. The general effect on public opinion was to discredit fundamentalism. This reaction together with the death, shortly after its conclusion, of Bryan, the only fundamentalist leader who was a national figure, resulted in the gradual subsidence of fundamentalism as a militant political movement.

To many sincerely religious people the controversy between fundamentalism and modernism posed a real dilemma. When read literally much of the Bible was to them incredible, and yet the modernists were making so many concessions to "the spirit of the age" that they seemed to have abandoned also the real substance of Christianity. As Charles A. Bennett in his book, *The Dilemma of Religious Knowledge*, expressed it, "To take religious knowledge as literally true is impossible, yet to assign it merely symbolic value is disastrous for religion." This conviction was deepened as, with the onset of the depression and the growing threat of another world war, the optimistic belief in automatic progress began to evaporate. Even leaders of the modernists began to have their doubts. One of the most influential, Harry Emerson Fosdick, in a sermon entitled *Beyond Modernism* said:

[1] While there were and are Roman Catholic "fundamentalists," no comparable struggle occurred within that Church because (1) Pope Pius X had condemned modernism in all its many forms in the encyclical *Pascendi Dominici Gregis* (1907) and (2) Catholic theologians make a distinction between the Divine inspiration and the literal interpretation of the Bible which enables a Catholic to accept a theistic version of evolution. Belief in the theory of evolution is, of course, merely permissive, not mandatory, and in the case of man can apply only to the evolution of the human body, the human soul being directly created by God. Works dealing with the Catholic position are cited in the *Suggestions for Additional Reading*.

The church thus had to go as far as modernism but now the church must go beyond it. For even this brief rehearsal of its history reveals modernism's essential nature; it is primarily an adaptation, an adjustment, an accommodation of Christian faith to contemporary scientific thinking. It started by taking the intellectual culture of a particular period as its criterion and then adjusted Christian teaching to that standard. Herein lies modernism's shallowness and transiency: it arose out of a temporary intellectual crisis; it took a special type of scientific thinking as standard; it became an adaptation to, a harmonization with, the intellectual culture of a particular generation. That, however, is no adequate religion to represent the Eternal and claim the allegiance of the soul. Let it be a modernist who says that to you! Unless the church can go deeper and reach higher than that it will fail indeed.[2]

In Europe, where a similar reaction had been initiated by the Swiss pastor, Karl Barth, a "neo-orthodox" school of Biblical theology rapidly developed. Under the influence of Barth and his followers and in response to the social crisis produced by the depression some American theologians began to formulate a new orthodoxy of their own. Reinhold Niebuhr, a leader in this movement, would agree with the modernists that the basic problem is to restate the fundamental doctrines of Protestant Christianity in a way that will make them genuinely relevant to the conditions of modern life. And he would agree also that "Christian faith is still suffering from the obscurantist effort to guard its truths in an age of Darwinian science by defying the undisputed evidences which honorable and honest scientists have adduced." But he would add to this: "The curse of modern religion is that it is so busy adjusting itself to the modern mind that it can find no energy to challenge the modern conscience."

Niebuhr, and other religious thinkers who have gone "beyond Modernism," attempt to develop a position in which everything that the scientists may happen to discover is true while nothing that is genuinely significant for a Christian's faith need be abandoned. It is not surprising, therefore, that the "new orthodoxy" has had a rapidly growing influence within the Protestant churches.

The readings selected for this problem exemplify four positions, fundamentalism, modernism, the new orthodoxy, and hu-

[2] *The Christian Century,* 52 (1935), 1549–1550.

manism. George Santayana's brief statement of the Christian story serves as a preface. Next, the chapter entitled "The Coming of Darwinism" from Richard Hofstadter's *Social Darwinism in American Thought* recounts in some detail its reception in America by scientists and by theologians.

Henry Ward Beecher was the most popular and influential preacher of his generation. He was one of the first who attempted to combine the theory of evolution in its Spencer-Fiske version with the Christian doctrine. In his sermon "The Two Revelations," delivered in 1885, Beecher argues that there is "an ascending development" in nature which has gradually revealed God's purpose and that this evolutionary process has *also* occurred in the development of religion itself. The Bible he considers "a record of the gradual and progressive unfolding of human knowledge in respect to social and spiritual things." Thus a progressive religion can be accommodated to the progression of knowledge through scientific inquiry.

Jane Mander's clever squib, "A Diary of Evolution in a Small Country Town," is included to illustrate that demoralization of "modern youth" which roused the fundamentalists' crusade to purify America. The next two selections are from a group of statements on evolution and religion printed during 1922, when the fundamentalist movement was on the upswing, in the *New York Times.* It is William Jennings Bryan's contention that Darwinism is a mere "hypothesis" and that guesses are not science. Therefore it has no valid claim to credibility. On the other hand a belief in this unproved hypothesis produces agnosticism or atheism. To this Harry Emerson Fosdick, a leading modernist, replies that Darwinism is no mere guess but a solidly established and highly credible result of scientific inquiry; and that, in any case, the belief in it can do harm to anyone who takes an enlightened view of the Christian religion. Arthur Garfield Hays was, as an attorney for the Civil Liberties Union, one

CONTENTS

The Clash of Issues

Two Initial Reactions to the Theory:

What is Darwinism? It is Atheism.

CHARLES HODGE

Evolution is God's way of doing things.

JOHN FISKE

A Liberal Preacher Attempts Reconciliation:

Evolution, applied to religion, will influence it only as the hidden temples are restored, by removing the sands which have drifted in from the arid deserts of scholastic and medieval theologies. It will change theology, but only to bring out the simple temple of God in clearer and more beautiful lines and proportions.

HENRY WARD BEECHER

To Which a Fundamentalist Replies:

Theistic evolution may be defined as an anesthetic which deadens the patient's pain while atheism removes his religion.

WILLIAM JENNINGS BRYAN

The Conflict Becomes Political:

Be it Enacted, by the General Assembly of the State of Tennessee, that it shall be unlawful for any teacher in any of the universities, normals, and all other public schools in the State, which are supported in whole or in part by the public school funds of the State, to teach the theory that denies the story of the divine creation of man as taught in the Bible, and to teach instead that man has descended from a lower order of animals.

Finally, a Humanist Philosopher and a Neo-orthodox Theologian Proffer Opposing Resolutions of the Controversy:

Were we to admit that there is but one method for ascertaining fact and truth—that conveyed by the word "scientific" in its most general and generous sense—no discovery in any branch of knowledge and inquiry could then disturb the faith that is religious.

JOHN DEWEY

Religion had no right to insist on the scientific accuracy of its mythical heritage. From this position a retreat was necessary. That part of mythology which is derived from pre-scientific thought, which does not understand the causal relations in the natural and historical world, must naturally be sacrificed in a scientific age. But there is a permanent as well as a primitive myth in every great mythical heritage. This deals with aspects of reality which are supra-scientific rather than pre-scientific. Modernistic religion has been so thin on the whole because it did not understand this distinction and thus sacrificed what is abiding with what is primitive in religious myth.

REINHOLD NIEBUHR

George Santayana: THE CHRISTIAN EPIC

THERE was in the beginning, so runs the Christian story, a great celestial King, wise and good, surrounded by a court of winged musicians and messengers. He had existed from all eternity, but had always intended, when the right moment should come, to create temporal beings, imperfect copies of himself in various degrees. These, of which man was the chief, began their career in the year 4004 B.C., and they would live on an indefinite time, possibly, that chronological symmetry might not be violated, until A.D. 4004. The opening and close of this drama were marked by two magnificent tableaux. In the first, in obedience to the word of God, sun, moon, and stars, and earth with all her plants and animals, assumed their appropriate places, and nature sprang into being with all her laws. The first man was made out of clay, by a special act of God, and the first woman was fashioned from one of his ribs, extracted while he lay in a deep sleep. They were placed in an orchard where they often could see God, its owner, walking in the cool of the evening. He suffered them to range at will and eat of all the fruits he had planted save that of one tree only. But they, incited by a devil, transgressed this single prohibition, and were banished from that paradise with a curse upon their heads, the man to live by the sweat of his brow and the woman to bear children in labour. These children possessed from the moment of conception the inordinate natures which their parents had acquired. They were born to sin and to find disorder and death everywhere within and without them.

At the same time God, lest the work of his hands should wholly perish, promised to redeem in his good season some of Adam's children and restore them to a natural life. This redemption was to come ultimately through a descendant of Eve, whose foot should bruise the head of the serpent. But it was to be prefigured by many partial and special redemptions. Thus, Noah was to be saved from the deluge, Lot from Sodom, Isaac from the sacrifice, Moses from Egypt, the captive Jews from Babylon, and all faithful souls from heathen forgetfulness and idolatry. For a certain tribe had been set apart from the beginning to keep alive the memory of God's judgments and promises, while the rest of mankind, abandoned to its natural depravity, sank deeper and deeper into crimes and vanities. The deluge that came to punish these evils did not avail to cure them. "The world was renewed* and the earth rose again above the bosom of the waters, but in this renovation there remained eternally some trace of divine vengeance. Until the deluge all nature had been exceedingly hardy and vigorous, but by that vast flood of water which God had spread out over the earth, and by its long abiding there, all saps were diluted; the air, charged with too dense and heavy a moisture, bred ranker principles of corruption. The early constitution of the universe was

* Bossuet: Discours sur l'histoire universelle, Part II, Chap. 1.

From *The Life of Reason: Reason in Religion* by George Santayana, pp. 92–97; copyright 1905 by Charles Scribner's Sons, 1933 by George Santayana. Reprinted by permission of the publishers.

weakened, and human life, from stretching as it had formerly done to near a thousand years, grew gradually briefer. Herbs and roots lost their primitive potency and stronger food had to be furnished to man by the flesh of other animals. . . . Death gained upon life and men felt themselves overtaken by a speedier chastisement. As day by day they sank deeper in their wickedness, it was but right they should daily, as it were, stick faster in their woe. The very change in nourishment made manifest their decline and degradation, since as they became feebler they became also more voracious and blood-thirsty."

Henceforth there were two spirits, two parties, or, as Saint Augustine called them, two cities in the world. The City of Satan, whatever its artifices in art, war, or philosophy, was essentially corrupt and impious. Its joy was but a comic mask and its beauty the whitening of a sepulchre. It stood condemned before God and before man's better conscience by its vanity, cruelty, and secret misery, by its ignorance of all that it truly behoved a man to know who was destined to immortality. Lost, as it seemed, within this Babylon, or visible only in its obscure and forgotten purlieus, lived on at the same time the City of God, the society of all the souls God predestined to salvation; a city which, however humble and inconspicuous it might seem on earth, counted its myriad transfigured citizens in heaven, and had its destinies, like its foundations, in eternity. To this City of God belonged, in the first place, the patriarchs and the prophets who, throughout their plaintive and ardent lives, were faithful to what echoes still remained of a primeval revelation, and waited patiently for the greater revelation to come. To the same city belonged the magi who followed a star till it halted over the stable in Bethlehem; Simeon, who divined the present salvation of Israel; John the Baptist, who bore witness to the same and made straight its path; and Peter, to whom not flesh and blood, but the spirit of the Father in heaven, revealed the Lord's divinity. For salvation had indeed come with the fulness of time, not, as the carnal Jews had imagined it, in the form of an earthly restoration, but through the incarnation of the Son of God in the Virgin Mary, his death upon a cross, his descent into hell, and his resurrection at the third day according to the Scriptures. To the same city belonged finally all those who, believing in the reality and efficacy of Christ's mission, relied on his merits and followed his commandment of unearthly love.

All history was henceforth essentially nothing but the conflict between these two cities; two moralities, one natural, the other supernatural; two philosophies, one rational, the other revealed; two beauties, one corporeal, the other spiritual; two glories, one temporal, the other eternal; two institutions, one the world, the other the Church. These, whatever their momentary alliances or compromises, were radically opposed and fundamentally alien to one another. Their conflict was to fill the ages until, when wheat and tares had long flourished together and exhausted between them the earth for whose substance they struggled, the harvest should come; the terrible day of reckoning when those who had believed the things of religion to be imaginary would behold with dismay the Lord visibly coming down through the clouds of heaven, the angels blowing their alarming trumpets, all generations of the dead rising from their graves, and judgment without appeal passed on every man, to the edification of the universal company and his own unspeakable joy or confusion. Whereupon the blessed would enter eternal bliss with God their master and the wicked everlasting torments with the devil whom they served.

The drama of history was thus to close upon a second tableau: long-robed and beatified cohorts passing above, amid various psalmodies, into an infinite luminous space, while below the damned, howling, writhing, and half transformed into loathsome beasts, should be engulfed in a fiery furnace. The two cities, always opposite in essence, should thus be finally divided in existence, each bearing its natural fruits and manifesting its true nature.

Let the reader fill out this outline for himself with its thousand details; let him remember the endless mysteries, arguments, martyrdoms, consecrations that carried out the sense and made vital the beauty of the whole. Let him pause before the phenomenon; he can ill afford, if he wishes to understand history or the human mind, to let the apparition float by unchallenged without delivering up its secret.

Richard Hofstadter: THE COMING OF DARWINISM

To have lived when this prodigious truth was advanced, debated, established, was a rare privilege in the centuries. The inspiration of seeing the old isolated mists dissolve and reveal the convergence of all branches of knowledge is something that can hardly be known to the men of a later generation, inheritors of what this age has won.

JOHN FISKE

WHEN Charles Darwin's *The Origin of Species* dawned upon the world it aroused no such immediate furor in the United States as it did in England. A public sensation comparable to that stirred up in England by Huxley's famous clash with Wilberforce in June 1860 was impossible in America, where a critical election was beginning whose results would disrupt the Union and bring about a terrible Civil War. Although the first American edition of *The Origin of Species* was widely reviewed in 1860, the coming of the war obscured new developments in scientific thought for all but professional scientists and a few hardy intellectuals.

Here and there, however, in quiet studies remote from the glare of politics, the ideas that were in time to transform the intellectual life of the country began to be cultivated. Darwin's friend Asa Gray, the Harvard botanist, after painstaking study of an advance copy of *The Origin of Species* sent to him by the author, wrote a careful review for the *American Journal of Sciences and Arts*, and with admirable foresight prepared a series of articles to defend evolution from the forthcoming charges of atheism. A few men who were already acquainted with the pre-Darwinian evolutionary speculation of Herbert Spencer were laying the foundations for a popular campaign in behalf of evolutionary

Richard Hofstadter, *Social Darwinism in American Thought 1860–1915*, Revised Edition (The Beacon Press, Boston, 1955), pp. 13–30. Reprinted by permission of The American Historical Association.

science. A little-known resident of Salem named Edward Silsbee, trying to arouse American interest in Spencer's ambitious project for a systematic philosophy, had found an immediate response in two men who would in time take the lead in remolding American thought. The first, John Fiske, a Harvard undergraduate who had already delved deeper than some of his professors into scientific and philosophical literature, went into ecstasies at the sight of Spencer's grandiose prospectus. The second, Edward Livingston Youmans, a popular lecturer on scientific subjects and author of a widely used textbook in chemistry, secured through his connection with D. Appleton and Company a sympathetic American publisher for Spencer's works. When public attention turned to the problems raised by Darwinism, Fiske and Asa Gray led the movement to make evolution respectable, and Youmans became the self-appointed salesman of the scientific world-outlook.

Interest in the natural sciences grew rapidly. Articles in religious journals and popular magazines show that American readers were fast becoming absorbed in the evolution controversy during the years after the Civil War. To men of culture the idea of evolution, so startling to the popular mind, was hardly new. A man like Whitman, for example, could write of "this old theory, evolution, as broach'd anew, trebled, with indeed all devouring claims by Darwin." Some Americans were familiar with the historic tradition of speculative evolution, which had reached the point of violent controversy in the days of Cuvier, Geoffrey St. Hilaire, and Goethe. Sir Charles Lyell's *Principles of Geology* (1832), which paved the way for the development hypothesis, had been widely read in the United States; and Robert Chambers'

anonymously published *Vestiges of Creation* (American edition, 1845), a popular religious presentation of evolution, had received much attention.

The rise of biblical criticism and comparative religion, the general relaxation of fundamentalist faith encouraged by the liberal clergy, prepared many Americans for the acceptance of Darwinism. James Freeman Clarke's *Ten Great Religions,* a liberal study of world creeds, ran through twenty-two editions in the fifteen years after its first appearance in 1871. A comparable popularization of the new biblical scholarship appeared in 1891, when Washington Gladden published *Who Wrote the Bible?*

Many of the influences that brought independent thinkers to accept evolution were manifest in the early work of John Fiske. Although Fiske came from a conventionally religious New England family, his orthodoxy had been undermined by European science. Before entering Harvard he had eagerly read Alexander von Humboldt's multi-volumed *Cosmos,* an encyclopedic review of current attainments of science, written in the language of naturalism. For Fiske this book had been a revelation of almost religious intensity, an emotional experience strong enough to force the Civil War into the background. "What's a war," he wrote in April 1861, "when a fellow has 'Kosmos' on his shelf and 'Faust' on his table?" It was appropriate for Fiske to couple Humboldt with Goethe. More than any other American of his time, Fiske felt the Faustian urge to devour the entire realm of knowledge. This it was which sent him plowing through the works of the English scientific writers, Mill, Lewes, Buckle, Herschel, Bain, Lyell, and Huxley, impelled him to undertake the most strenuous exercises in philology (he had mastered eight languages and started six others by the time he was twenty), and kept him abreast of recent advances in biblical criticism. When Darwinism appeared, with its imposing answer to the riddle of species, when Spencer promised a profound and authoritative interpretation of the meaning of science, Fiske had long since changed gods.

Darwinism attracted many who lacked Fiske's ebullient spirit and his freakish appetite for learning. To young Henry Adams, bewildered by his recent experiences in Civil War diplomacy, it at first suggested an intelligible rationale for recent history:

He felt, like nine men in ten, an instinctive belief in Evolution . . . Natural Selection led back to Natural Evolution, and at last to Natural Uniformity. This was a vast stride. Unbroken Evolution under uniform conditions pleased everyone—except curates and bishops; it was the very best substitute for religion; a safe, conservative, practical, thoroughly Common-Law deity. Such a working system for the universe suited a young man who had just helped to waste five or ten thousand million dollars and a million lives, more or less, to enforce unity and uniformity on people who objected to it; the idea was only too seductive in its perfection; it had the charm of art.

For others, more confident of the optimistic implications of evolution, *The Origin of Species* became an oracle, consulted with the reverence usually reserved for Scripture. Charles Loring Brace, a leading social worker and reformer, read it thirteen times and emerged with the assurance that evolution guaranteed the final fruition of human virtue and the perfectibility of man. "For if the Darwinian theory be true, the law of natural selection applies to all the moral history of mankind, as well as the physical. Evil

must die ultimately as the weaker element, in the struggle with good."

Before it could secure a grip on the public mind and find a place in accepted patterns of thought, evolution had to prevail within the realm of science itself; and even scientists, especially those among the older generation who were committed to traditional ways of thinking, found adjustment to evolution a painful process. "It is like confessing murder," Darwin had remarked in 1844, when first he broached to Joseph Dalton Hooker his belief in the mutability of species. And Sir Charles Lyell, whose geology led to the very brink of the development hypothesis, hesitated for almost a decade before making the plunge. Before Darwin, however, scientists had been puzzled by the inadequacy of the old notion of the fixity of species, which fitted so badly with the facts of paleontology and geology, with known fossil specimens, the wide variety of species, and the classification of living organisms. They had conventionally assumed that a series of acts of special creation had taken place. While this facile hypothesis may have accorded with their religious beliefs, the new generation of scientists, trained to see their function as a quest for natural causes, suspected that special creation was a poor intellectual makeshift. Among this generation the development hypothesis and the theory of natural selection spread rapidly, and a host of distinguished Darwinian advocates was soon in the field.

Alone among outstanding American naturalists, Louis Agassiz refused to the bitter end to accept Darwinism or evolution in any form. Agassiz's master, Georges L. Cuvier, had been the leading opponent of evolution in the early nineteenth century, and the pupil fought Darwin as his teacher had fought Lamarck. To Agassiz, Darwinism was a crude and insolent challenge to the eternal verities, objectionable as science and abominable for its religious blasphemies. In his last article, published posthumously, Agassiz argued that all the evolution known to man is ontogenetic, the embryological development of the individual. Beyond this it would be impossible to go; evidence of descent of later from earlier species, or of the animal ancestry of man, was totally lacking. The classification of animals, Agassiz said, belied the idea of progression from lower to higher; the history of geological succession showed that the lowest in structure is not necessarily the first in time. A great diversity of animal types probably existed from the very beginning; it is therefore more likely that what men call species arose through separate successive acts of creation of differing individual organisms rather than natural selection or any other mode of purely natural development.

Convinced that Darwinism was a fad (like Oken's *Naturphilosophie* in his younger days), Agassiz brashly asserted that he would "outlive this mania"; but when he died in 1873 American science lost its last distinguished opponent of the new theory. Even if Agassiz had lived many years longer it is doubtful that his influence would have retarded the spread of evolution among scientists. Before his death his own students were falling away. Among them, Joseph Le Conte felt that outlines of the development theory were latent in Agassiz's own classification of animal forms, which need only be interpreted dynamically to yield a convincing picture of the evolutionary past. William James, who had been intimate with Agassiz, was his bitterest critic. "The more I think of Darwin's ideas," he wrote to his brother Henry in

1868, "the more weighty do they appear to me, though of course my opinion is worth very little—still, I *believe* that that scoundrel Agassiz is unworthy either intellectually or morally for him to wipe his shoes on, and I find a certain pleasure in yielding to the feeling." Not long after Agassiz's death, a writer pointed out that eight of Agassiz's most eminent pupils at Harvard, including the master's own son, were evolutionists of relatively long standing. In 1874, James Dwight Dana, dean of American geologists, published the final edition of his *Manual of Geology*, in which he too, after a prolonged attempt to resist natural selection, at last granted his endorsement.

Asa Gray soon found himself the acknowledged interpreter of American scientific opinion. Combining the conviction of a crusader with the caution of a scientist, Gray was peculiarly fitted to lead the Darwinian forces. His initial review of *The Origin of Species*, a brilliant essay upon the entire problem, had given American biologists a favorable but measured summary of Darwin's case. Conscientiously Gray had set forth what he conceived were the most cogent scientific objections to natural selection, but he praised the theory for its rigidly scientific contribution to biology. Darwin, he wrote guardedly, "has rendered a theory of derivation [of species] much less improbable than before. . . . Such a theory chimes in with the established doctrines of physical science, and is not unlikely to be largely accepted before it can be proved." With more daring he attacked Agassiz's theory of species as "theistic to excess" and praised Darwin's as an antidote. Closing on a note of defiance to possible religious criticisms, he declared that Darwinism is perfectly compatible with theism; and, he conceded, while it is also compatible with atheism, "that is true of physical theories generally." Natural selection, far from being an attack upon the argument from design in nature, may be considered one of the possible theories of the workings of God's plan.

By the early 1870's the transmutation of species and natural selection dominated the outlook of American naturalists. At the twenty-fifth meeting of the American Association for the Advancement of Science, Vice-President Edward S. Morse gave a striking review of contributions of American biologists to evidences of evolution, which showed that their reception of Darwinism had been more than passive. Most impressive among these were studies by Professor Othniel C. Marsh of Yale. An acquaintance of Gray, Lyell, and Darwin, one of the most colorful scientific men of the period, Marsh had set out in the early years of the decade in search of fossil specimens to confirm the development hypothesis. By 1874 he had collected a striking set of American fossil horses and published a paper, tracing the development of the horse through geologic ages, which Darwin later acclaimed as the best support of evolution appearing in the two decades following *The Origin of Species.*

II

The conversion of the scientists promised early success in the universities, where the atmosphere was charged with electricity. A reform movement was under way to put greater stress upon science in the curricula, and science schools were being established to meet the country's growing need for technicians. The appalling neglect of scientific specialization (which had brought forth in the smaller colleges such monstrosities as "Professor of Natural Philosophy, Chemistry, Mineralogy, and Geology and Lecturer of Zoölogy and Botany") was now a patent anachronism in a nation that urgently needed science for its industry and agriculture and could well afford to patronize scientific development.

Harvard led the way in university reform with the appointment in 1869 of Charles William Eliot, a chemist, as its president. At Eliot's inauguration John Fiske privately expressed the hope that this appointment would signify the end of "old fogyism" at Harvard. The realization of this wish came sooner than he expected, and in a more personal way, when Eliot immediately called upon him to offer a series of special lectures at Harvard on the philosophy of science. Eight years before, as an undergraduate, Fiske had been threatened with dismissal from Harvard College if he were caught talking Comtism, which was generally considered atheistic. Now he was asked to hold forth at length under the aegis of the university on the positivist philosophy. Fiske, who had long since dropped Comte in favor of Spencer, undertook the task of defending Spencer against the charge of plagiarizing from Comte, but this hardly diminished the sweetness of his own vindication. The lectures, which were reported in the papers, aroused some criticism, but the audiences were large and enthusiastic. Some years later, when William James used Spencer's *Principles of Psychology* as a textbook at Harvard, there was not a murmur of excitement. The new philosophy had made its way into the oldest of American universities quickly and almost without controversy.

At Yale it was again Spencer rather than Darwin who created the issue, which did not arise until 1879–80, when William Graham Sumner clashed with President Noah Porter. Porter, a Congregational clergyman, was not an uncompromising opponent of evolutionism in all its forms. Influenced by Professor Marsh's discoveries and his prestige, and impressed by the fine collection of specimens at Yale's own Peabody Museum, he had surrendered to evolution by 1877, when he gave an address in which he asserted that he found "no inconsistency between the findings of this museum on the one corner and the teachings of the college chapel on the other." Nonetheless, he believed that American colleges should be kept "distinctively and earnestly Christian." When Sumner, also converted to evolution by Marsh's work, tried to use Spencer's *Study of Sociology* as a text in one of his courses, Porter objected to the work's antitheistic and anticlerical tone, and insisted that Sumner abandon it. A widely publicized controversy followed, which ended in a Pyrrhic victory for Porter. Sumner, after excoriating Porter, threatened to resign, and was induced with some difficulty to remain. He dropped Spencer's book, on the ground that the controversy had undermined its value as a textbook, but otherwise continued in his independent ways. Porter himself conducted a course in "First Principles" to refute Spencer's ideas, in which he used some of the evolutionist's writings. To his dismay, the appeal of Spencer's works was irresistible to many students, and they became converts to the doctrines Porter was at such pains to overthrow.

Less prominent scholars and clerical teachers in some other schools of higher learning were neither as safe nor as successful as Fiske and Sumner. The geologist Alexander Winchell was dismissed from Vanderbilt in 1878, and occasional infringements of academic liberties in other institutions, North and South, caught the attention of the public throughout the 1880's and 1890's. What is perhaps most noteworthy, however, is not the strength of the resistance but the rapidity with which the new ideas won their way in the better colleges and universities. Evolution penetrated the ranks of faculties and students alike. "Ten or fifteen years ago," declared Whitelaw Reid in an address at Dartmouth College in 1873, "the staple subject here for reading and talk, outside study hours, was English poetry and fiction. Now it is English science. Herbert Spencer, John Stuart Mill, Huxley, Darwin, Tyndall, have usurped the places of Tennyson and Browning, and Matthew Arnold and Dickens."

The founding in 1876 of The Johns Hopkins University, an institution devoted to research and free of obligations to any religious denomination, marked a long forward step in higher education. Its first president, Daniel Coit Gilman, struck a symbolic note of defiance to obscurantism at its opening ceremonies by having Thomas Henry Huxley, who was in America on a lecture tour, give an address. Huxley's address was well received, but his appearance called forth the expected *odium theologicum*. *"It was bad enough to invite Huxley,"* wrote one divine. *"It were better to have asked God to be present. It would have been absurd to ask them both."* Such outcries, however, did not impede the development of the new institution, which was soon among the few leading unversities in the advancement of scientific learning. Nor did the cries of alarm obscure or diminish Huxley's popularity; he found it necessary to refuse countless requests for lectures, and his comings and goings were reported with lavish care by the press.

Popular magazines promptly opened their columns to the evolution controversy. Characteristic progress over a ten-year period from hostility to skepticism to gingerly approval, and finally to full-blown praise, can be seen in the volumes of the *North American Review*, traditional forum of New England intellectuals. In 1860 an anonymous reviewer of *The Origin of Species*, arguing that natural selection would take an eternity of time to accomplish its task, rejected Darwin's theory as "fanciful." Four years later a writer pointed out that the development hypothesis, as a general conception, "has much to recommend it to the speculative mind. It is, as it were, an abstract statement of the order which the intellect expects to find in nature." In 1868, the freethinker Francis Ellingwood Abbot suggested that despite differences of opinion on minor points the development hypothesis would probably take a place among the accepted truths of science. In 1870 natural selection was praised by Charles Loring Brace as "one of the great intellectual events of the present century, influencing every department of investigation." The following year the magazine published an essay by Chauncey Wright defending natural selection; this so impressed Darwin that he had it reprinted in pamphlet form for English readers.

At the instance of Youmans, who saw the need for a popular magazine emphasizing scientific news, D. Appleton and Company founded *Appleton's Journal* in 1867. The journal was the first to run large numbers of articles on Spencer and Darwin and to provide regular publication for the popularizations of Youmans and Fiske. Neither wholly literary nor wholly scientific, *Appleton's Journal* pleased few readers. More successful was the *Popular Science Monthly*, founded by Youmans in 1872. The monthly was surprisingly well received, considering the difficulty of some of its subject matter, and soon sold eleven thousand copies a month. There, next to more sensational sketches designed to satisfy common curiosity—"Great Fires and Rainstorms," "Hypnotism in Animals," "The Genesis of Superstition," "Earthquakes and Their Causes"—were learned articles on the philosophy of science, laudatory sketches of leading scientists, discussions of the reconciliation between science and religion, polemics against obscurantism, and reports on the latest progress of research. Edited on a high level and followed faithfully by a substantial body of readers, the monthly was the signal journalistic accomplishment of the scientific revival. To Youmans also must be given credit for organizing on behalf of Appleton's the famous International Scientific Series, a set of books by outstanding scientific figures of the time planned to cover almost the whole range of natural and social knowledge, which numbered among its contributors Walter Bagehot, John W. Draper, Stanley Jevons, Spencer, and Edward Tylor in the social sciences; Alexander Bain, Joseph Le Conte, Darwin, and Henry Maudsley in psychology and biology; and John Tyndall and others in physical science. Through the International Scientific Series, the *Popular Science Monthly*, and its control of American editions of Spencer's writings, Appleton dominated the new intellectual movement and rose to unchallenged leadership in the publishing world on the tidal wave of evolutionism.

The *Atlantic Monthly* also exploited the controversy by publishing Asa Gray's early defenses of Darwinism. Seeking to maintain a noncommittal tone on Darwinism throughout the 1860's, the editors balanced the scale by printing one of Agassiz's counterblasts; but in 1872 an editorial on the rejection of Darwin by the French Academy of Science spoke of natural selection as having

. . . quite won the day in Germany and England, and very nearly won it in America. If the highest type of scientific mind be that which unites the power of originating grand generalizations with endless patience and caution in verifying them, then it is not too much to say that since the death of Newton this type has been in no one more perfectly realized than in Mr. Darwin.

E. L. Godkin's *Nation* gave a favorable if none too conspicuous place to notices of evolutionary writings. Its reviewers were among the first to praise Darwin, Wallace, and Spencer. Gray's unsigned notices occasionally graced its columns, and some of his most vigorous onslaughts against recalcitrant naturalists and presumptuous clergymen appeared there. At a time when clerical magazines were in an uproar over Darwin's *The Descent of Man,* the *Nation* described it as "the most lucid and impartial exposition of the present state of scientific opinion respecting the origin of man and his relations to the lower animals."

There could be no better testimony to an overwhelming interest in scientific developments and the new rationalism than the extensive daily newspaper coverage, in generous detail, of scientific or philosophical lectures. Fiske's Harvard lectures on "The Cosmic Philosophy" were reported in the New York *World* at the suggestion of the editor, Manton Marble. Huxley's lectures in New York were reprinted and discussed in the *Tribune,* and his visit was treated as ceremoniously as that of royalty. It excited no surprise that George Ripley, one of the more vocal journalistic champions of Darwinism, should take the dedication of the new *Tribune* building as an occasion for a muddy discussion of the metaphysi-

cal implications of nineteenth-century science. The "universal drenching" of belles-lettres and journalism with natural selection amused an editor of the *Galaxy.* "Journalism is dyed so deep with it," he remarked, "that the favorite logic of the leading articles is 'survival of the fittest' and the favorite jest is 'sexual selection.'" He noticed that a Washington reporter for the *Herald* had recently done a sketch of the Senate in which members were portrayed in Darwinian terms as bulls, lions, foxes, and rats. At the latest New Orleans Mardi Gras the Missing Link had been used as a costume motif.

III

The last citadels to be stormed were the churches, where evolution won its chief victories among the intellectually alert members of the more liberal Protestant denominations. Of course large numbers of devout persons, Protestant and Catholic, were untouched by Darwinism. Probably the most popular religious leader of the Gilded Age was the evangelist Dwight L. Moody, whose followers must have been blissfully ignorant about all of the troublesome questions raised by the new science. The persistence of fundamentalism into the twentieth century is a token of the incompleteness of the Darwinian conquest. Among the reflective congregations of the late nineteenth-century churches, however, there were vague emotional stirrings and intellectual dissatisfactions which helped to create a receptive frame of mind for a theology liberal enough to embrace the concept of evolution.

Darwinism seemed to strike from more than one direction at the very heart of traditional theology. For nearly a century the argument from design, as popularized by the English theologian William Paley, had been standard proof of the existence of God. Now it seemed to many that Darwinism, by blasting at this theological foundation stone, must inevitably lead to atheism. The new theory also exploded traditional conceptions of sin, and with them the moral sanctions of the past. At the very least it clearly impaired the authority of Scripture by discrediting the Genesis version of the creation. Such was the initial orthodox reaction. The appearance of *The Descent of Man* (1871) heaped fuel on the fires of clerical wrath, for now human dignity itself was openly under attack. Religious readers pointed with horror at Darwin's too vivid description of man's ancestor as "a hairy quadruped, furnished with a tail and pointed ears, probably arboreal in habits."

Darwin's work and everything connected with it aroused virulent hostility throughout the 1860's and 1870's. Not a few of the clerical arguments were on the intellectual plane of the minister who asserted that Darwinism would be established only when scientists could take a monkey from the zoo and by natural selection make him into a man. The tone became such that a clergyman, Professor W. N. Rice of Wesleyan University, remonstrated with his fellows against their attitude toward Darwin and suggested that they confine their criticism to the scientific issues.

The most important clerical objection, of course, was that Darwinism could not be reconciled with theism. Such was the central theme of the most popular exposition of anti-Darwinian views, Charles Hodge's *What Is Darwinism?* (1874). An old-school clergyman, author of one of the most imposing theological treatises of the time, and editor of the *Princeton Review,* Hodge could speak with author-

ity for a large body of churchmen. In his polemical volume, Hodge reminded his readers that "the Bible has little charity for those who reject it. It pronounces them to be either derationalized or demoralized, or both." The perilous paths of atheism threaten all who trifle with evolution, he declared, citing a formidable list of alleged materalists and atheists, including Darwin, Haeckel, Huxley, Büchner, and Vogt. With scant regard for facts, Hodge charged that Darwin had carefully excluded any suggestion of design from nature, and closed with the assertion that Darwinism and atheism are synonymous.

Catholic critics were often equally intransigent. Although mindful that St. George Mivart, an English Catholic and an able critic of natural selection, was an evolutionist, Orestes A. Brownson probably expressed the prevailing Catholic reaction when he urged a policy of no compromise with evolutionary biology. Dissatisfied with the weaker negations of both Protestant and many Catholic opponents of Darwinism, Brownson called for a categorical repudiation of nineteenth-century geology and biology, which he said represented a regression from the science of Aquinas. Lyell, Darwin, Huxley, Spencer, even Agassiz, came under his vigorous attack. "The *differentia* of man," he wrote, in an Aristotelian analysis of *The Descent of Man,* "not being in the ape, cannot be obtained from the ape by development. This sufficiently refutes Darwin's whole theory." The Genesis version of creation is still in possession, he concluded, and must be maintained until the contrary is fully demonstrated; the burden of proof therefore lies with Darwin.

The most orthodox struggled with the desperation of men who felt their cause was doomed, but others retired to defensible positions in comparatively good order. The ultimate collapse of uncompromising opposition to evolution was foreshadowed as early as 1871, when James McCosh, the president of Princeton University and the semi-official voice of American Presbyterianism, acknowledged his acceptance of the development hypothesis in his *Christianity and Positivism.* An outstanding proponent of the current religious philosophy known as Scotch or "common sense" realism, and a man of unquestioned Christian integrity, McCosh had been specially imported from Scotland to give tone to Princeton. It was therefore a matter of considerable moment when, in a volume written to defend theism by the argument from design, he accepted the development hypothesis and conceded that natural selection is at least a portion of the truth:

Darwinism cannot be regarded as settled. . . . I am inclined to think that the theory contains a large body of important truths which we see illustrated in every department of organic nature; but that it does not contain the whole truth, and that it overlooks more than it perceives. . . . That this principle [natural selection] is exhibited in nature and working to the advancement of plants and animals from age to age, I have no doubt. . . . But it has not been proven that there is no other principle at work.

True, McCosh balked at the application of natural selection to mankind on the ground that a special act of creation explains more plausibly man's unique spiritual features; but the damage to orthodoxy was now done. Youmans wrote to Spencer in 1871:

Things are going here furiously. I have never known anything like it. Ten thousand *Descent of Man* have been printed and I guess they are nearly all gone. . . . The progress of liberal thought is remarkable. Everybody is asking for explanations. The clergy are in a flutter. McCosh told them not to worry, as whatever might be discovered he would find design in it and put God behind it. Twenty-five clergymen of Brooklyn sent for me to meet them of a Saturday night and tell them what they should do to be saved. I told them they would find the way of life in the Biology and in the *Descent of Man.* They said "very good," and asked me to come again at the next meeting of the clerical club, to which I went and was again handsomely resoluted.

The weekly *Independent,* the most influential religious paper in the country, with over six thousand clergymen on its mailing list, was among the first to give a relatively favorable hearing to evolution. Its initial review of *The Origin of Species* intimated that the book tended to displace the Creator from "the animated universe," but acknowledged the wealth of scientific material it contained. Subsequently the book was recommended for "the careful study of theologians and men of science." The paper was cautious and still under the influence of Agassiz in the late 1860's, although it had by then receded to the position that Darwinism would not affect theism, an acknowledgment which always served as an opening wedge. About this time, however, attempts at tenuous reconciliation of evolution with Scripture began to appear. "So long as the Bible does not assert that species were created distinct by an authoritative fiat we may be allowed to hear with no fluttering of our theologic nerves, the speculations of zoologists," wrote one reviewer. By 1880 the *Independent* had completely reversed itself and had begun to publish full-throated polemics on behalf of evolution. Other periodicals were slower to modify their views, but two decades after the introduction of Darwinism, some change was noticeable among even the most conservative. The *New Englander,* an important forum of Yankee clergymen which had at first charged Darwin with reviving "an old, exploded theory," in 1883 published an interesting conciliatory article, in which the hysteria of some Christian apologists was admitted. "A fresh source of conviction," declared the writer, "is opened to our anticipations of immortality. It is the flattest inconsistency for an evolutionist to deny the probability of a higher future life."

In the task of easing the transition to Darwinism for their brethren, liberal clergymen received aid and comfort from men of science. Asa Gray labored tirelessly to show that natural selection had no ultimate bearing on the argument from design, and that Darwin himself was explicitly theistic. To those who insisted that the origins of species be left in the realm of the supernatural, Gray replied that they were arbitrarily limiting the field of science without enlarging that of religion. Joseph Le Conte, in his *Religion and Science,* a collection of Bible-class lectures, followed Gray in maintaining that the argument from design could not be changed by any possible answer to the question whether there had been transmutation of species or what the process of evolution might be. Science, he urged, should be looked upon not as the foe of religion, but rather as a complementary study of the ways in which the First Cause operated in the natural world. Whatever science might learn, the existence of God as First Cause could always be assumed. Liberal theologians made good use of the fact that many of the advocates of evolution, like Le Conte, Dana, and McCosh, were men of undeniable Christian piety. They

stood as personal symbols of the possibility of reconciling religion and science.

The most important pulpit in the United States was brought within the evolutionary ranks when Henry Ward Beecher was converted, thanks to the combined impact of Darwin and Spencer. Through Beecher's *Christian Union,* which at one time reached a circulation of 100,000, and the *Outlook,* edited by Lyman Abbott, his successor at Plymouth Church, the liberalizing influence of Beecher's new theology was widespread. To the reconciliation of religion and science Beecher brought his national reputation, his brilliant, artful rhetoric, and the healthy good cheer of a man newly liberated from the confines of Puritan theology. His chief theoretical contribution was a carefully elaborated distinction between the science of theology and the art of religion: theology would be corrected, enlarged, and liberated by evolution, but religion, as a spiritual fixture in the character of man, would be unmoved. Declaring himself "a cordial Christian evolutionist," Beecher publicly acknowledged Spencer as his intellectual foster father. It was Beecher who translated the solution of the design problem into the idioms of a business civilization, with the reminder that "design by wholesale is grander than design by retail." Lyman Abbott agreed; moreover, he forswore the traditional notion of sin, which, he held, degraded God as well as man. He proposed to replace it with an evolutionary view in which every immoral act was to be regarded as a lapse into animality. Sin would then be as abhorrent as ever, but the libel on God implied in the doctrine of original sin would be no more.

By the 1880's, the lines of argument that would be taken in the reconciliation of science and religion had become clear.

Religion had been forced to share its traditional authority with science, and American thought had been greatly secularized. Evolution had made its way into the churches themselves, and there remained not a single figure of outstanding proportions in Protestant theology who still ventured to dispute it. But evolution had been translated into divine purpose, and in the hands of skillful preachers religion was livened and refreshed by the infusion of an authoritative idea from the field of science. The ranks of the old foes soon could hardly be distinguished as they merged in common hostility to pessimism or skepticism about the promise of American life. The specter of atheism was no longer a menace, and surveys of the colleges where one would most expect to discover infidelity revealed how little there was. With little exaggeration a minister could say that American infidelity had not produced "a single champion of cosmopolitan or even of national reputation." "The

spirit," explained Phillips Brooks, "that cries 'Credo quia impossibile,' the heroic spirit of faith, is too deep in human nature for any one century to eradicate it." For was it not true, as Beecher told his Plymouth Church congregation, that "the moral structure of the human mind is such that it must have religion"? He continued:

It must have superstition, or it must have intelligent religion. It is just as necessary to men as reason is, as imagination is, as hope and desire are. Religious yearning is part and parcel of the human composition. And when you have taken down any theologic structure—if you should take down the Roman Church and scatter its materials; if then one by one you should dissect all Protestant theologies and scatter them—man would still be a religious animal, would need and be obliged to go about and construct some religious system for himself.

To these sentiments of its leading divine, the Gilded Age gave unanimous consent.

Henry Ward Beecher: THE TWO REVELATIONS

"All things were made by Him, and without Him was not anything made that was made."—John i:3.

THAT the whole world and the universe were the creation of God is the testimony of the whole Bible, both Jewish and Christian; but how he made them—whether by the direct force of a creative will or indirectly through a long series of gradual changes—the Scriptures do not declare. The grand truth is that this world was not a chance, a creative fermentation, a self-development, but that it was the product of an Intelligent

Being, that the divine will in the continuance of this world manifests itself under the form of what are called natural laws, and that the operations of normal and legitimate laws are the results of divine will.

There are two records of God's creative energy. One is the record of the unfolding of *man* and of the race under the inspiration of God's nature: this is a mere sketch; of the ancient periods of man there is almost nothing known. The other of these records or revelations—if you choose to call them so—pertains to the physical globe, and reveals the divine

From *Evolution and Religion* (New York: Fords, Howard, and Hulbert, 1885), pp. 44–55.

thought through the unfolding history of *matter;* and this is the older. So we have two revelations: God's thought in the evolution of matter, and God's thought in the evolution of mind; and these are the Old Testament and the New—not in the usual sense of those terms, but in an appropriate scientific use of them.

In that great book of the Old there is a record of the progress, order, and result of God's thought in regard to the globe as a habitation for man. Though not every stage, yet the chief stages of preparation of this dwelling for man have been discovered and are now being deciphered and read. The crude, primitive material of the world of matter, the igneous condition, the aqueous stages, the dynamic and chemical periods, the gradual formation of the soil, the mountain-building, the dawn of life, vegetable and animal, the stages of their progress—are not all these things written in the scientific revelation of God's history of creation? When I reflect upon the range of the invisible and the silent God, with the vast and well-nigh incomprehensible stretch of time, and of his compassionate waiting and working through illimitable ages and periods, compared with which a million years as marked by the clock are but seconds; when I reflect that the silent stones and the buried strata contain the record of God's working, and that the globe itself is a sublime history of God as an engineer and architect and as a master-builder, I cannot but marvel at the indifference with which good men have regarded this stupendous revelation of the ages past, and especially at the assaults made by Christian men upon scientific men who are bringing to light the long-hidden record of God's revelation in the material world.

With what eagerness has the world heard of the discovery in Egypt of the tomb that contained the buried kings of the Pharaohnic dynasty! But what are all these mighty kings, wrapped for three thousand years in the shroud of silence, compared with the discovery of God's method and the results of creation millions of centuries ago, retained in the rocks? Were the two tables of stone, written by the finger of God, a memorial to be revered, and their contents to be written in letters of gold in all men's churches, and yet his ministers and priests turn with indifference or with denunciation, even with scorn, sometimes, from the literature of the rocks written by the hand of God all over the earth? What were the Ten Commandments but a paragraph out of the book of the divine revelation of nature? Ages before Sinai itself was upheaved in the progress of divine world-building; ages before the human race was enough advanced to have made the Ten Commandments possible, God was slowly moulding the world that was to contain within itself its own history. Science is but the deciphering of God's thought as revealed in the structure of this world; it is a mere translation of God's primitive revelation. If to reject God's revelation of the Book is infidelity, what is it to reject God's revelation of himself in the structure of the whole globe? There is as much infidelity in regard to the great history that science unfolds today, as there is in regard to the record of the Book—and more! The primitive prefatory revelation of the structural thought of God in preparing a dwelling for the human race —is that nothing? Man had a cradle represented to antiquity as the poetical Eden; but the globe itself had a different Eden, one of fire, convulsions, clouds and storms, of grinding ice and biting chemistry preparing the soil.

To be sure, the history of man in the

Bible is more important than the history of the globe. The globe was created for man as a house is created to serve the family. But both are God's revelations; both are to be received with intelligent reverence; both are to be united and harmonized; both are to be employed in throwing light, the one upon the other. That noble body of investigators who are deciphering the hieroglyphics of God inscribed upon this temple of the earth are to be honored and encouraged. As it is now, vaguely bigoted theologians, ignorant pietists, jealous churchmen, unintelligent men, whose very existence seems like a sarcasm upon creative wisdom, with leaden wit and stinging irony swarm about the adventurous surveyors who are searching God's handiwork and who have added to the realm of the knowledge of God the grandest treasures. Men pretending to be ministers of God, with all manner of grimace and shallow ridicule and witless criticism and unproductive wisdom, enact the very feats of the monkey in the attempt to prove that the monkey was not their ancestor.

It is objected to all assertions of the validity of God's great record in matter, that science is uncertain and unripe; that men are continually changing the lines of science, that it will not do to rest upon the results of scientific investigation. It will be time to consider science when it has ripened into a certainty, say men, but not now. Well, as the case stands, how is the record of the book any more stable and intelligible than the record of the rock? The whole Christian world for two thousand years, since the completion of the canons, has been divided up like the end of a broom into infinite splinters, quarreling with each other as to what the book did say, and what it did mean. Why then should men turn and say that scientific men are unsettled

in their notions? At the congress of Christian churches in Hartford recently, the Rev. Dr. Hopkins, a prominent high-churchman, said: "No less than nineteen different varieties of Christianity are at present trying to convert the Japanese. The nineteen do not agree as to what the ministry is, nor as to the word, some including the Apocrypha, and others discarding it altogether; and many differing as to the meaning of the Scriptures. Nor are they agreed as to the Sacraments. So too on doctrine, discipline, and worship. There are all sorts of contradictions of belief. Now, if Christians, with eighteen centuries of accumulated tradition cannot agree, how can we expect the heathen to solve the great riddle?" This is not mine, but I give a hearty Amen to it, and only find fault with it because it is not strong enough. When men, therefore, attempt to pour ridicule upon the legitimate deductions of scientific investigation, that have passed through the periods of trial, discussion, and proof, as if they were less praiseworthy than the declarations of the written revelation, I say to them, " No ground can be less tenable than such a ground as yours if we will look at the way in which the written revelation is misunderstood, and into the infinite splittings and divisions which men have made in attempting to interpret what is said to be the more stable revelation of the truth."

It is said, or thought, that a layman should not meddle with that which can be judged by only scientific experts: that science demands a special training before one can discern correctly its facts, or judge wisely of the force of its conclusions. This is true; it is true both of those who accept and those who deny its results. But, when time and investigation have brought the scientific world to an agreement, and its discoveries pass into the hands of all men, there comes an important duty, which moral teachers, parents, and especially clergymen, are perhaps as well or better fitted to fulfill than mere scientists, viz., to determine what effect the discoveries of science will have upon questions of morality and religion. It is to this aspect that the best minds of the Christian ministry are now addressing themselves.

It may be well before going further to expose some popular errors regarding the Evolutionary philosophy—now so widely accepted by the scientific world —and to point out some of the changes which it will work out in the schools of theology, as a new interpreter of God's two revelations.

A vague notion exists with multitudes that science is infidel, and that Evolution in particular is revolutionary—that is, revolutionary of the doctrines of the Church. Men of such views often say, " I know that religion is true. I do not wish to hear anything that threatens to unsettle my faith." But faith that can be unsettled by the access of light and knowledge had better be unsettled. The intensity of such men's faith in their own thoughts is deemed to be safer than a larger view of God's thoughts. Others speak of Evolution as a pseudo-science teaching that man descended from monkeys, or ascended as the case may be. They have no conception of it as the history of the divine process in the building of this world. They dismiss it with jests, mostly ancient jests; or, having a smattering of fragmentary knowledge, they address victorious ridicule to audiences as ignorant as they are themselves.

Now the ascent of man from the anthropoid apes is a mere hypothesis. It has not been proved; and in the broader sense of the word "proved," I see certainly no present means of proving it. It stands in the region of hypothesis, pressed forward by a multitude of probabilities. The probabilities are so many, and the light which this hypothesis throws upon human history and human life and phenomena is such that I quite incline to the supposition that it is, in the order of nature, in analogy with all the rest of God's work, and that in the ascending scale there was a time unknown, and methods not yet discovered, in which man left behind his prior relatives, and came upon the spiritual ground which now distinguishes him from the whole brute creation. Of one thing I am certain, that whatever may have been the origin, it does not change either the destiny or the moral grandeur of man as he stands in the full light of civilization today. The theory of the evolution of the human race from an inferior race, not proved and yet probable, throws light upon many obscure points of doctrine and of theology that have most sadly needed light and solution.

First, then, what is Evolution, and what does it reveal? The theory of Evolution teaches that the creation of this earth was not accomplished in six days of twenty-four hours; that the divine method occupied ages and ages of immense duration; that nothing, of all the treasures of the globe as they now stand, was created at first in its present perfectness; that everything has grown through the lapse of ages into its present condition; that the whole earth, with their development in it, was, as it were, an egg, a germ, a seed; that the forests, the fields, the shrubs, the vineyards, all grasses and flowers, all insects, fishes, and birds, all mammals of every gradation, have had a long history, and that they have come to the position in which they now stand through ages and ages of gradual change and unfolding. Also that the earth itself went through a period of long preparation, passing from ether by condensation to a visible cloud form with increasing solidity, to such a condition as now prevails in the sun; that it condensed and became solid; that cold congealed its vapor; that by chemical action and by mechanical grinding of its surface by ice a soil was prepared fit for vegetation, long before it was fit for animal life; that plants simple and coarse came first and developed through all stages of complexity to the present conditions of the vegetable kingdom; that aquatic, invertebrate animals were the earliest of animals, according to the testimony of fossils in the earth. Fishes came next in order, then amphibians, then reptiles. " All these tribes were represented by species before the earliest of the mammals appeared. The existence of birds before the earliest mammal is not proved, though believed by some paleontologists upon probable evidence. The early mammals were marsupial, like the opossum and the kangaroo, and lived in the same era called by Agassiz the reptilian period. True mammals came into geologic history in the tertiary era. Very long after the appearance of the first bird came man, the last and grandest of the series, it is doubtful whether in the tertiary period or immediately sequent. It is not established whether his bones or relics occur as far back as the tertiary era."

This is a very brief statement, not my own, but that of Professor Dana, of renown. No man is more trusted, more careful, more cautious than he, and this brief history of the unfolding series I have taken bodily from his writings.

Second. As thus set forth, it may be said that Evolution is accepted as *the* *method* of creation by the whole scientific world, and that the period of controversy is passed and closed. A few venerable men yet live, with many doubts; but it may be said that ninety-nine per cent—as has been declared by an eminent physicist—ninety-nine per cent of scientific men and working scientists of the world are using this theory without any doubt of its validity. While the scientific world is at agreement upon this *order* of occurrence, it has been much divided as to the *causes* which have operated to bring about these results. There is a diversity of opinion still, but with every decade scientific men are drawing together to a common ground of belief.

Third. The theory of Evolution is the *working* theory of every department of physical science all over the world. Withdraw this theory, and every department of physical research would fall back into heaps of hopelessly dislocated facts, with no more order or reason or philosophical coherence than exists in a basket of marbles, or in the juxtaposition of the multitudinous sands of the seashore. We should go back into chaos if we took out of the laboratories, out of the dissecting-rooms, out of the fields of investigation, this great doctrine of Evolution.

Fourth. This science of Evolution is taught in all advanced academies, in all colleges and universities, in all medical and surgical schools, and our children are receiving it as they are the elements of astronomy or botany or chemistry. That in another generation Evolution will be regarded as uncontradictable as the Copernican system of astronomy, or the Newtonian doctrine of gravitation, can scarcely be doubted. Each of these passed through the same contradiction by theologians. They were charged by the Church, as is Evolution now, with fostering materialism, infidelity, and atheism. We know what befell Galileo for telling the truth of God's primitive revelation. We know, or do not know, at least, how Newton stood charged with infidelity and with atheism when he announced the doctrine of gravitation. Who doubts the heliocentric theory today? Who doubts whether it is the sun which is moving round the earth or the earth round the sun? Who doubts that the law of attraction, as developed by Newton, is God's material law universally? The time is coming when the doctrine of Evolution, or the method of God in the creation of the world, will be just as universally accepted as either of these great physical doctrines. The whole Church fought them; yet they stand, conquerors.

Fifth. Evolution is substantially held by men of profound Christian faith: by the now venerable and universally honored scientific teacher, Professor Dana of Yale College, a devout Christian and communicant of a Congregational Church; by Professor Le Conte of the University of California, an elder in the Presbyterian Church; by President McCosh of Princeton College, a Presbyterian of the Presbyterians, and a Scotch Presbyterian at that; by Professor Asa Gray of Harvard University, a communicant of the Christian Church; by increasing numbers of Christian preachers in America; by Catholics like Mivart, in England; by Wallace, a Christian not only, but of the spiritualistic school; by the Duke of Argyle, of the Scotch Presbyterian Church; by Ground, an ardent admirer of Herbert Spencer and his whole theory, though rejecting his agnosticism—an eminent and leading divine in the Church of England; and finally, among hundreds of other soundly learned and Christian men, by the Bishop of London, Dr. Williams, whose Bampton Lectures for 1884 contain a bold, frank, and judicial estimate of Evolution, and its relations to Christianity.

Sixth. To the fearful and the timid let me say, that while Evolution is certain to oblige theology to reconstruct its system, it will take nothing away from the grounds of true religion. It will strip off Saul's unmanageable armor from David, to give him greater power over the giant. Simple religion is the unfolding of the best nature of man toward God, and man has been hindered and embittered by the outrageous complexity of unbearable systems of theology that have existed. If you can change theology, you will emancipate religion; yet men are continually confounding the two terms, religion and theology. They are not alike. Religion is the condition of a man's nature as toward God and toward his fellow-men. That is religion—love that breeds truth, love that breeds justice, love that breeds harmonies of intimacy and intercommunication, love that breeds duty, love that breeds conscience, love that carries in its hand the scepter of pain, not to destroy and to torment, but to teach and to save. Religion is that state of mind in which a man is related by his emotions, and through his emotions by his will and conduct, to God and to the proper performance of duty in this world. Theology is the philosophy of God, of divine government, and of human nature. The philosophy of these may be one thing; the reality of them may be another and totally different one. Though intimately connected, they are not all the same. Theology is a science; religion, an art.

Evolution will multiply the motives and facilities of righteousness, which was and is the design of the whole Bible.

It will not dull the executive doctrines of religion, that is, the forms of them by which an active and reviving ministry arouses men's consciences, by which they inspire faith, repentance, reformation, spiritual communion with God. Not only will those great truths be unharmed, by which men work zealously for the reformation of their fellow-men, but they will be developed to a breadth and certainty not possible in their present philosophical condition. At present the sword of the spirit is in the sheath of a false theology. Evolution, applied to religion, will influence it only as the hidden temples are restored, by removing the sands which have drifted in from the arid deserts of scholastic and medieval theologies. It will change theology, but only to bring out the simple temple of God in clearer and more beautiful lines and proportions.

Seventh. In every view of it, I think we are to expect great practical fruit from the application of the truths that flow now from the interpretation of Evolution. It will obliterate the distinction between natural and revealed religion, both of which are the testimony of God; one, God's testimony as to what is best for man in his social and physical relations, and the other, what is best for man in his higher spiritual nature. What is called morality will be no longer dissevered from religion. Morals bear to spirituality the same relation which the root bears to the blossom and the fruit. Hitherto a false and imperfect theology has set them in two different provinces. We have been taught that morality will not avail us, and that spirituality is the only saving element: whereas, there is no spirituality itself without morality; all true spirituality is an outgrowth, it is the blossom and fruit on the stem of morality. It is time that these distinctions were

obliterated, as they will be, by the progress and application of the doctrine of Evolution.

In every view, then, it is the duty of the friends of simple and unadulterated Christianity to hail the rising light and to uncover every element of religious teaching to its wholesome beams. Old men may be charitably permitted to die in peace, but young men and men in their prime are by God's providence laid under the most solemn obligations to thus discern the signs of the times, and to make themselves acquainted with the knowledge which science is laying before them. And above all, those zealots of the pulpit—who make faces at a science which they do not understand, and who reason from prejudice to ignorance, who not only will not lead their people, but hold up to scorn those who strive to take off the burden of ignorance from their shoulders—these men are bound to open their eyes and see God's sun shining in the heavens.

That Evolution applied will greatly change the reading and the construction of the earlier periods of the Scripture history cannot be doubted. The Bible itself is one of the most remarkable monuments of the truth of the Evolutionary process. There has been an immense amount of modern ignorance imported into the Bible. Again the Lord is turning out the money-changers, and those who sell oxen and doves, from the temple. But that operation of old left the temple cleansed and pure for religious uses. With many thoughtful Christian men, large tracts of the Bible lie uncultivated and unused. They do not use the whole; yet if any should take out a single text there would be screams of fear. There is not one Christian man in a hundred, nor in a thousand, that thinks that the whole Bible is necessary to his spiritual development and growth. Men pick and choose, and, in a sort of unconscious way, reject portions constantly. We must save them from throwing it all over. For the growth of knowledge, and of intelligence, will not permit men any longer to hold it as a talisman, an idol; and unless guided by a wiser teaching they will reject the Sacred Scriptures not only as false in science, but as a guide to conduct and to character!

We of this age have come to the mountain-top; yet we can only see the promised land of the future. Our children shall go over to the land flowing with milk and honey. Great has been the past; the future shall be yet greater. Instead of doubts and dread of ill-omened prophecies, and railings and murmurings, the Church should write upon her banner in this day of the orient, "Rise, shine; Thy light has come. The glory of the Lord is risen upon thee."

The last years of my life I dedicate to this work of religion, to this purpose of God, to this development, on a grander scale, of my Lord and Master Jesus Christ. I believe in God. I believe in immortality. I believe in Jesus Christ as the incarnated representative of the spirit of God. I believe in all the essential truths that go to make up morality and spiritual religion. I am neither an infidel, nor an agnostic, nor an atheist; but if I am anything, by the grace of God I am a lover of Jesus Christ, as the manifestation of God under the limitations of space and matter; and in no part of my life has my ministry seemed to me so solemn, so earnest, so fruitful, as this last decade will seem if I shall succeed in uncovering to the faith of this people the great truths of the two revelations—God's building revelation of the material globe, and God's building revelation in the unfolding of the human mind. May God direct me in your instruction!

Jane Mander: A DIARY OF EVOLUTION

IN A SMALL COUNTRY TOWN

Age

5–12   Accept Bible as written, God, Christ, and The Angels *in toto*, Fixed Heaven and Hell, the Good and the Bad.

12–14   Believe Bible "inspired," but not all "literal." Shed Fixed Hell. See Satan as Force of Evil. Doubt Divinity of Christ.

14–16   Read Bible as history and legend. Shed Divinity of Christ, and The Angels. Keep God as Love, Justice, and Father of Mankind. Have fixed ideas of Right and Wrong, but become interested in the Bad.

16–18   Browning stage. Frame "God's in His Heaven, All's Right With the World." Parade aggressive Optimism. Accept "World as it is." Preach Duty of Cheerfulness, etc. Orthodox as to Poverty and the Working Classes.

18–19   Honest Doubt. Learn Omar Khayyám by heart. Shed

Jane Mander, "A Diary of Evolution," *The New Republic*, Vol. VI, No. 73, March 25, 1916, pp. 211–212. Reprinted by permission of *The New Republic*.

Heaven. Question Personal God. Put away "God's in His Heaven." More liberal as to Sin.

19–22 General mental tangle. Study Theosophy and Reincarnation, Spiritualism and Christian Science. Shed Personal God. Call Him Force, the First Cause, the Guiding Principle, Universal Law, etc. Believe in Mind Over Matter, and Love as Constructive Force. Shed fixed ideas of Right and Wrong. See Sin as Defective Education. Morality the new religion. Frame Henley's "Invictus." Exalt The Self. Believe in Human Nature. Get first glimmer of Evolution. Hear vaguely of Socialism. Realize The Brotherhood of Man with due regard for Classes and Types.

IN NEW YORK

22–23 Discover Bernard Shaw. Shed everything else.

23–25 Plunge into psychology, biology, history. Doubt everything but Scientific Facts. Shed God in any form. Learn the Relativity of Truth. Meet Socialists. Investigate Sex War and Wage War. Have Temperament. Exalt the Intellect. Despise the Average Person. Put "Invictus" away in a drawer.

25–26 Begin again. The new religion—socialism; the new god—humanity; the new Christ—the man, the carpenter; the new devils—poverty, capitalism; the new heaven and hell—the earth; the new Bible—Marx, Wells, The Fabian Society, The Economists; the new sins

—ignorance, indifference; the new temples—the street corner, the lecture hall; the new idealism—*liberté, égalité, fraternité;* the new words—Individualism, Communism, Humanitarianism.

26–28 Preach Radicalism, Anarchism, Agitation, and No Compromise. Despise Laws, Ceremonies, Traditions, and Precedents. Believe in Free Love. Exalt Sincerity. Proclaim The Facts of Life. Lose Temperament in the flurry of general destruction. Tolerate all Comrades in the March of Progress. Believe in The People and the Natural Rights of Man.

28–30 Doubt adequacy of Anarchism. Begin to suspect The People. Consider Organization, Cooperation, and Education. Study Unions and Statistics. See need for Some Compromise. Shed Anarchism and Agitation.

30–32 Join a union. Believe in the Wage War. Preach Unity and Sacrifice for the Good of All. Lead Strikes.

32–33 Doubt possibility of Unity. Suspect motives of leaders. Question effectiveness of Sacrifice. Hazy as to definition of The Good of All. Lose illusions about The People. See hope in Political Action. Shed Unions and The Working Man.

33–34 Go into politics. Learn the value of Compromise. Suspect the wisdom of Sincerity. Drop Free Love. Uphold Laws and Ceremonies. Hide The Facts of Life. Try Merit and Reason upon the politician. Suspect the power of Merit and Reason. Try Money and Influence upon the politician. Perceive their immediate and decisive effect. Suspect possibility of Democracy as defined by Lincoln. Suspect the politician. Suspect myself. Begin to feel tired.

34–35 Shed politics and the politician. Turn to Social Service. Join four Clubs and three Movements. Boost the Feminists and Suffragists. Talk, and listen to talk. Begin to suspect Movements. Suspect all Human Nature. Get more tired.

35–36 A great weariness. Sick of Action. Sick of Words. Sick of Humanity. No illusions left. Shed everything. Do nothing. Turn to Art.

36–37 Believe in Art. Recover Temperament, but don't mention it. Fall in love with an artist. Believe in love. Believe in the artist. Get married.

37 Have a child, who will begin it all over again.

Gail Kennedy

William Jennings Bryan: GOD AND EVOLUTION

I appreciate your invitation to present the objections to Darwinism, or evolution applied to man, and beg to submit to your readers the following:

The only part of evolution in which any considerable interest is felt is evolution applied to man. A hypothesis in regard to the rocks and plant life does not affect the philosophy upon which one's life is built. Evolution applied to fish, birds and beasts would not materially affect man's view of his own responsibilities except as the acceptance of an unsupported hypothesis as to these would be used to support a similar hypothesis as to man. The evolution that is harmful—distinctly so—is the evolution that destroys man's family tree as taught by the Bible and makes him a descendant of the lower forms of life. This, as I shall try to show, is a very vital matter.

I deal with Darwinism because it is a definite hypothesis. In his "Descent of Man" and "Origin of Species" Darwin has presumed to outline a family tree that begins, according to his estimate, about two hundred million years ago with marine animals. He attempts to trace man's line of descent from this obscure beginning up through fish, reptile, bird and animal to man. He has us descend from European, rather than American, apes and locates our first ancestors in Africa. Then he says, "But why speculate?"—a very significant phrase because it applies to everything that he says. His entire discussion is speculation.

Darwin's "Laws"

Darwin set forth two (so-called) laws by which he attempts to explain the changes which he thought had taken place in the development of life from the earlier forms to man. One of these is called "natural selection" or "survival of the fittest," his argument being that a form of life which had any characteristic that was beneficial had a better

From *The New York Times*, February 26, 1922. Reprinted by permission of *The New York Times*.

chance of survival than a form of life that lacked that characteristic. The second law that he assumed to declare was called "sexual selection," by which he attempted to account for every change that was not accounted for by natural selection. Sexual selection has been laughed out of the class room. Even in his day Darwin said (see note to "Descent of Man" 1874 edition, page 625) that it aroused more criticism than anything else he had said, when he used sexual selection to explain how man became a hairless animal. Natural selection is being increasingly discarded by scientists. John Burroughs just before his death, registered a protest against it. But many evolutionists adhere to Darwin's *conclusions* while discarding his *explanations*. In other words, they accept the line of descent which he suggested *without any explanation whatever* to support it.

Other scientists accept the family tree which he outlined, but would have man branch off to a point below, or above, the development of apes and monkeys instead of coming through them. So far as I have been able to find, Darwin's line of descent has more supporters than any other outlined by evolutionists. If there is any other clearly defined family tree supported by a larger number of evolutionists, I shall be glad to have information about it that I may investigate it.

The first objection to Darwinism is that it is only a guess and was never anything more. It is called a "hypothesis," but the word "hypothesis," though euphonious, dignified and high-sounding, is merely a scientific synonym for the old-fashioned word "guess." If Darwin had advanced his views as a *guess* they would not have survived for a year, but they have floated for a half a century, buoyed up by the inflated word

"hypothesis." When it is understood that "hypothesis" means "guess," people will inspect it more carefully before accepting it.

No Support in the Bible

The second objection to Darwin's guess is that it has not one syllable in the Bible to support it. This ought to make Christians cautious about accepting it without thorough investigation. The Bible not only describes man's creation, but gives a reason for it; man is a part of God's plan and is placed on earth for a purpose. Both the Old and New Testament deal with man and with man only. They tell of God's creation of him, of God's dealings with him and of God's plans for him. Is it not strange that a Christian will accept Darwinism as a substitute for the Bible when the Bible not only does not support Darwin's hypothesis but directly and expressly contradicts it?

Third—Neither Darwin nor his supporters have been able to find a fact in the universe to support their hypothesis. With millions of species, the investigators have not been able to find *one single instance* in which one species has changed into another, although, according to the hypothesis, *all* species have developed from one or a few germs of life, the development being through the action of "resident forces" and without outside aid. Wherever a form of life, found in the rocks, is found among living organisms, there is no material change from the earliest form in which it is found. With millions of examples, nothing imperfect is found—nothing in the process of change. This statement may surprise those who have accepted evolution without investigation, as most of those who call themselves evolutionists have done. One preacher who wrote to me expressing great regret that I should dissent from Darwin said that he had not investigated the matter for himself, but that nearly all scientists seemed to accept Darwinism.

The latest word that we have on this subject comes from Professor Bateson, a high English authority, who journeyed all the way from London to Toronto, Canada, to address the American Association for the Advancement of Science the 28th day of last December. His speech has been published in full in the January issue of *Science*.

Professor Bateson is an evolutionist, but he tells with real pathos how every effort to discover the origin of species has failed. He takes up different lines of investigation, commenced hopefully but ending in disappointment. He concludes by saying, "Let us then proclaim in precise and unmistakable language that our faith in evolution is unshaken," and then he adds, "our doubts are not as to the reality or truth of evolution, but as to the origin of species, a technical, almost domestic problem. Any day that mystery may be solved." Here is optimism at its maximum. They fall back on faith. They have not yet found the origin of species, and yet how can evolution explain life unless it can account for change in species? Is it not more rational to believe in creation of man by separate act of God than to believe in evolution without a particle of evidence?

Fourth—Darwinism is not only without foundation, but it compels its believers to resort to explanations that are more absurd than anything found in the "Arabian Nights." Darwin explains that man's mind became superior to woman's because, among our brute ancestors, the males fought for their females and thus strengthened their minds. If he had lived until now, he would not have felt it necessary to make so ridiculous an explanation, because woman's mind is not now believed to be inferior to man's.

As To Hairless Men

Darwin also explained that the hair disappeared from the body, permitting man to become a hairless animal because, among our brute ancestors, the females preferred the males with the least hair and thus in the course of ages, bred the hair off. It is hardly necessary to point out that these explanations conflict; the males and the females could not both select at the same time.

Evolutionists, not being willing to accept the theory of creation, have to explain everything, and their courage in this respect is as great as their efforts are laughable. The eye, for instance, according to evolutionists, was brought out by "the light beating upon the skin"; the ears came out in response to "air waves"; the leg is the development of a wart that chanced to appear on the belly of an animal; and so the tommyrot runs on *ad infinitum* and sensible people are asked to swallow it.

Recently a college professor told an audience in Philadelphia that a baby wiggles its big toe without wiggling its other toes because its ancestors climbed trees; also that we dream of falling because our forefathers fell out of trees fifty thousand years ago, adding that we are not hurt in our dreams of falling because we descended from those that were *not killed*. (If we descended from animals at all, we certainly did not descend from those that were killed in falling.) A professor in Illinois has fixed as the great day in history the day when a water puppy crawled upon the land and decided to stay there, thus becoming man's first progenitor. A dispatch from

Paris recently announced that an eminent scientist had reported having communicated with the soul of a dog and learned that the dog was happy.

I simply mention these explanations to show what some people can believe who cannot believe the Bible. Evolution seems to close the heart of some to the plainest spiritual truths while it opens the mind to the wildest of guesses advanced in the name of science.

Guessing Is Not Science

Guesses are not science. Science is classified knowledge, and a scientist ought to be the last person to insist upon a guess being accepted until proof removes it from the field of hypothesis into the field of demonstrated truth. Christianity has nothing to fear from any *truth*; no *fact* disturbs the Christian religion or the Christian. It is the unsupported *guess* that is substituted for science to which opposition is made, and I think the objection is a valid one.

But, it may be asked, why should one object to Darwinism *even though it is not true?* This is a proper question and deserves a candid answer. There are many guesses which are perfectly groundless and at the same time entirely harmless; and it is not worth while to worry about a guess or to disturb the guesser so long as his guess does not harm others.

The objection to Darwinism is that it is *harmful*, as well as groundless. It entirely changes one's view of life and undermines faith in the Bible. Evolution has no place for the miracle or the supernatural. It flatters the egotist to be told that there is nothing that his mind cannot understand. Evolution proposes to bring all the processes of nature within the comprehension of man by making it the explanation of everything that is

known. Creation implies a Creator, and the finite mind cannot comprehend the infinite. We can understand some things, but we run across mystery at every point. Evolution attempts to solve the mystery of life by suggesting a process of development commencing "in the dawn of time" and continuing uninterrupted up until now. Evolution does not explain creation: it simply diverts attention from it by hiding it behind eons of time. If a man accepts Darwinism, or evolution applied to man, and is consistent, he rejects the miracle and the supernatural as impossible. He commences with the first chapter of Genesis and blots out the Bible story of man's creation, not because the evidence is insufficient, but because the miracle is inconsistent with evolution. If he is consistent, he will go through the Old Testament step by step and cut out all the miracles and all the supernatural. He will then take up the New Testament and cut out all the supernatural—the virgin birth of Christ, His miracles and His resurrection, leaving the Bible a story book without binding authority upon the conscience of man. Of course, not all evolutionists are consistent; some fail to apply their hypothesis to the end just as some Christians fail to apply their Christianity to life.

Evolution and God

Most of the evolutionists are materialists; some admitting that they are atheists, others calling themselves agnostics. Some call themselves "theistic evolutionists," but the theistic evolutionist puts God so far away that He ceases to be a present influence in the life. Canon Barnes of Westminster, some two years ago, interpreted evolution as to put God back of the time when the electrons came out of "stuff" and combined (about

1740 of them) to form an atom. Since then, according to Canon Barnes, things have been developing to God's plan but without God's aid.

It requires measureless credulity to enable one to believe that all that we see about us came by chance, by a series of happy-go-lucky accidents. If only an infinite God could have formed hydrogen and oxygen and united them in just the right proportions to produce water—the daily need of every living thing—scattered among the flowers all the colors of the rainbow and every variety of perfume, adjusted the mocking bird's throat to its musical scale, and fashioned a soul for man, why should we want to imprison God in an impenetrable past? This is a living world. Why not a living God upon the throne? Why not allow Him to work now?

Theistic evolutionists insist that they magnify God when they credit Him with devising evolution as a plan of development. They sometimes characterize the Bible God as a "carpenter god," who is described as repairing His work from time to time at man's request. The question is not whether God could have made the world according to the plan of evolution—of course, an all-powerful God could make the world as He pleased. The real question is, Did God use evolution as His plan? If it could be shown that man, instead of being made in the image of God, is a development of beasts we would have to accept it, regardless of its effect, for truth is truth and must prevail. But when there is no proof we have a right to consider the effect of the acceptance of an unsupported hypothesis.

Darwin's Agnosticism

Darwinism made an agnostic out of Darwin. When he was a young man he believed in God; before he died he declared that the beginning of all things is a mystery insoluble by us. When he was a young man he believed in the Bible; just before his death he declared that he did not believe that there had ever been any revelation; that banished the Bible as the inspired Word of God, and, with it, the Christ of whom the Bible tells. When Darwin was young he believed in a future life; before he died he declared that each must decide the question for himself from vague, uncertain probabilities. He could not throw any light upon the great questions of life and immortality. He said that he "must be content to remain an agnostic."

And then he brought the most terrific indictment that I have read against his own hypothesis. He asks (just before his death): "Can the mind of man, which has, as I fully believe, been developed from a mind as low as that possessed by the lowest animal, be trusted when it draws such grand conclusions?" He brought man down to the brute level and then judged man's mind by brute standards.

This is Darwinism. This is Darwin's own testimony against himself. If Darwinism could make an agnostic of Darwin, what is its effect likely to be upon students to whom Darwinism is taught at the very age when they are throwing off parental authority and becoming independent? Darwin's guess gives the student an excuse for rejecting the authority of God, an excuse that appeals to him more strongly at this age than at any other age in life. Many of them come back after a while as Romanes came back. After feeding upon husks for twenty-five years, he began to feel his way back, like a prodigal son, to his father's house, but many never return.

Professor Leuba, who teaches psychology at Bryn Mawr, Pennsylvania, wrote a book about six years ago entitled "Belief in God and Immortality" (it can be obtained from the Open Court Publishing Company, Chicago), in which he declared that belief in God and immortality is dying out among the educated classes. As proof of this he gave the results which he obtained by submitting questions to prominent scientists in the United States. He says that he found that more than half of them, according to their own answers, do not believe in a personal God or a personal immortality. To reinforce his position, he sent questions to students of nine representative colleges and found that unbelief increases from 15 per cent in the freshman year to 30 per cent in the junior class, and to 40 to 45 per cent (among the men) at graduation. This he attributes to the influence of the scholarly men under whose instruction they pass in college.

Religion Waning Among Children

Anyone desiring to verify these statistics can do so by inquiry at our leading state institutions and even among some of our religious denominational colleges. Fathers and mothers complain of their children losing their interest in religion and speaking lightly of the Bible. This begins when they come under the influence of a teacher who accepts Darwin's guess, ridicules the Bible story of creation and instructs the child upon the basis of the brute theory. In Columbia a teacher began his course in geology by telling the children to lay aside all that they had learned in Sunday School. A teacher of philosophy in the University of Michigan tells students that Christianity is a state of mind and that there are only two books of literary value in the Bible. Another professor in

that university tells students that no thinking man can believe in God or in the Bible. A teacher in the University of Wisconsin tells his students that the Bible is a collection of myths. Another state university professor diverts a dozen young men from the ministry and the president of a prominent state university tells his students in a lecture on religion to throw away religion if it does not harmonize with the teaching of biology, psychology, etc.

The effect of Darwinism is seen in the pulpits; men of prominent denominations deny the virgin birth of Christ and some even His resurrection. Two Presbyterians, preaching in New York state, recently told me that agnosticism was the natural attitude of old people. Evolution naturally leads to agnosticism. Those who teach Darwinism are undermining the faith of Christians; they are raising questions about the Bible as an authoritative source of truth; they are teaching materialistic views that rob the life of the young of spiritual values.

Christians do not object to freedom of speech; they believe that Biblical truth can hold its own in a fair field. They concede the right of ministers to pass from belief to agnosticism or atheism, but they contend that they should be honest enough to separate themselves from the ministry and not attempt to debase the religion which they profess.

And so in the matter of education. Christians do not dispute the right of any teacher to be agnostic or atheistic, but Christians do deny the right of agnostics and atheists to use the public school as a forum for the teaching of their doctrines.

The Bible has in many places been excluded from the schools on the ground that religion should not be taught by those paid by public taxation. If this doctrine is sound, what right have the enemies of religion to teach irreligion in the public schools? If the Bible cannot be taught, why should Christian taxpayers permit the teaching of guesses that make the Bible a lie? A teacher might just as well write over the door of his room, "Leave Christianity behind you, all ye who enter here," as to ask his students to accept a hypothesis directly and irreconcilably antagonistic to the Bible.

Our opponents are not fair. When we find fault with the teaching of Darwin's unsupported hypothesis, they talk about Copernicus and Galileo and ask whether we shall exclude science and return to the dark ages. Their evasion is a confession of weakness. We do not ask for the exclusion of any scientific truth, but we do protest against an atheist teacher being allowed to blow his guesses in the face of the student. The Christians who want to teach religion in their schools furnish the money for denominational institutions. If atheists want to teach atheism, why do they not build their own schools and employ their own teachers? If a man really believes that he has brute blood in him, he can teach that to his children at home or he can send them to atheistic schools, where his children will not be in danger of losing their brute philosophy, but why should he be allowed to deal with other people's children as if they were little monkeys?

We stamp upon our coins "In God We Trust"; we administer to witnesses an oath in which God's name appears, our President takes his oath of office upon the Bible. Is it fanatical to suggest that public taxes should not be employed for the purpose of undermining the nation's God? When we defend the Mosaic account of man's creation and contend that man has no brute blood in him, but was made in God's image by separate act and placed on earth to carry out a divine decree, we are defending the God of the Jews as well as the God of the Gentiles, the God of the Catholics as well as the God of the Protestants. We believe that faith in a Supreme Being is essential to civilization as well as to religion and that abandonment of God means ruin to the world and chaos to society.

Let these believers in "the tree man" come down out of the trees and meet the issue. Let them defend the teachings of agnosticism or theism if they dare. If they deny that the natural tendency of Darwinism is to lead many to a denial of God, let them frankly point out the portions of the Bible which they regard as consistent with Darwinism, or evolution applied to man. They weaken faith in God, discourage prayer, raise doubt as to a future life, reduce Christ to the stature of a man, and make the Bible a "scrap of paper." As religion is the only basis of morals, it is time for Christians to protect religion from its most insidious enemy.

Harry Emerson Fosdick:

A REPLY TO MR. BRYAN IN THE NAME OF RELIGION

THE editor of *The Times* has asked me to reply to Mr. Bryan's statement on "God and Evolution." I do so, if only to voice the sentiments of a large number of Christian people who in the name of religion are quite as shocked as any scientist could be in the name of science at Mr. Bryan's sincere but appalling obscurantism.

So far as the scientific aspect of the discussion is concerned, scientists may well be left to handle it. Suffice it to say that when Mr. Bryan reduces evolution to a hypothesis and then identifies a hypothesis with a "guess" he is guilty of a sophistry so shallow and palpable that one wonders at his hardihood in risking it. A guess is a haphazard venture of opinion without investigation before or just reason afterward to sustain it; it is a *jeu d'esprit*. But a hypothesis is a seriously proffered explanation of a difficult problem ventured when careful investigation of facts points to it, retained as long as the discovered facts sustain it, and surrendered as soon as another hypothesis enters the field which better explains the phenomena in question.

Every universally accepted scientific truth which we possess began as a hypothesis, is in a sense a hypothesis still, and has become a hypothesis transformed into a settled conviction as the mass of accumulating evidence left no questions as to its substantial validity. To call evolution, therefore, a guess is one thing; to tell the truth about it is another, for to tell the truth involves recognizing the tireless patience with which generations of scientists in every appropriate field of inquiry have been investigating all discoverable facts that bear upon the problem of mutation of species, with substantial unanimity as to the results so far as belief in the hypothesis of evolution is concerned. When Darwin, after years of patient, unremitting study, ventured his hypothesis in explanation of evolution—a hypothesis which was bound to be corrected and improved—one may say anything else one will about it except to call it a "guess." That is the one thing which it certainly was not. Today, the evolutionary hypothesis, after many years of pitiless attack and searching investigation, is, as a whole, the most adequate explanation of the facts with regard to the origin of species that we have yet attained, and it was never so solidly grounded as it is today. Dr. Osborn is making, surely, a safe statement when he says that no living naturalist, so far as he knows, "differs as to the immutable truth of evolution in the sense of the continuous fitness of plants and animals to their environment and the ascent of all the extinct and existing forms of life, including man, from an original and single cellular state."

The Real Situation

When, therefore, Mr. Bryan says, "Neither Darwin nor his supporters have been able to find a fact in the universe to

From *The New York Times*, March 12, 1922. Reprinted by permission of *The New York Times*.

support their hypothesis," it would be difficult to imagine a statement more obviously and demonstrably mistaken. The real situation is that every fact on which investigation has been able to lay its hands helps to confirm the hypothesis of evolution. There is no known fact which stands out against it. Each newly discovered fact fits into an appropriate place in it. So far as the general outlines of it are concerned, the Copernican astronomy itself is hardly established more solidly.

My reply, however, is particularly concerned with the theological aspects of Mr. Bryan's statement. There seems to be no doubt about what his position is. He proposes to take his science from the Bible. He proposes, certainly, to take no science that is contradicted by the Bible. He says, "Is it not strange that Christians will accept Darwinism as a substitute for the Bible when the Bible not only does not support Darwin's hypothesis, but directly and expressly contradicts it?" What other interpretation of such a statement is possible except this: that the Bible is for Mr. Bryan an authoritative textbook in biology—and if in biology, why not in astronomy, cosmogony, chemistry or any other science, art, or concern of man whatever? One who is acquainted with the history of theological thought gasps as he reads this. At the close of the sixteenth century a Protestant theologian set down the importance of the Book of Genesis as he understood it. He said that the text of Genesis "must be received strictly"; that "it contains all knowledge, human and divine"; that "twenty-eight articles of the Augsburg Confession are to be found in it"; that "it is an arsenal of arguments against all sects and sorts of atheists, pagans, Jews, Turks, Tartars, Papists, Calvinists, Socinians and Baptists"; that it is "the source of all science and arts, including law, medicine, philosophy

and rhetoric," "the source and essence of all histories and of all professions, trades and works," "an exhibition of all virtues and vices," and "the origin of all consolation."

One had supposed that the days when such wild anachronisms could pass muster as good theology were passed, but Mr. Bryan is regalvanizing into life that same outmoded idea of what the Bible is and proposes in the twentieth century that we shall use Genesis, which reflects the pre-scientific view of the Hebrew people centuries before Christ as an authoritative textbook in science, beyond whose conclusions we dare not go.

Martin Luther and Bryan

Why, then, should Mr. Bryan complain because his attitude toward evolution is compared repeatedly, as he says it is, with the attitude of the theological opponents of Copernicus and Galileo? On his own statement, the parallelism is complete. Martin Luther attacked Copernicus with the same appeal which Mr. Bryan uses. He appealed to the Bible. He said: "People gave ear to an upstart astrologer who strove to show that the earth revolves, not the heavens or the firmament, the sun and the moon. Whoever wishes to appear clever must devise some new system, which of all systems is, of course, the very best. This fool wishes to reverse the entire science of astronomy, but sacred Scripture tells us that Joshua commanded the sun to stand still, and not the earth."

Nor was Martin Luther wrong if the Bible is indeed an authoritative textbook in science. The denial of the Copernican astronomy with its moving earth can unquestionably be found in the Bible if one starts out to use the Bible that way—"The world also is established, that it cannot be moved" (Psalm 93:1); "Who laid the foundations of the earth, that it should not be moved forever" (Psalm 104:5). Moreover, in those bygone days, the people who were then using Mr. Bryan's method of argument did quote these passages as proof, and Father Inchofer felt so confident that he cried,

> The opinion of the earth's motion is of all heresies the most abominable, the most pernicious, the most scandalous; the immovability of the earth is thrice sacred; argument against the immortality of the soul, the existence of God, and the incarnation should be tolerated sooner than an argument to prove that the earth moves.

Indeed, as everybody knows who has seriously studied the Bible, that book represents in its cosmology and its cosmogony the view of the physical universe which everywhere obtained in the ancient Semitic world. The earth was flat and was founded on an underlying sea (Psalm 136:6; Psalm 24:1–2; Genesis 7:11); it was stationary; the heavens, like an upturned bowl, "strong as a molten mirror" (Job 37:18; Genesis 1:6–8; Isaiah 40:22; Psalm 104:2), rested on the earth beneath (Amos 9:6; Job 26:11); the sun, moon and stars moved within the firmament of special purpose to illumine man (Genesis 1:14–19); there was a sea above the sky, "the waters which were above the firmament" (Genesis 1:7; Psalm 148:4) and through "the windows of heaven" the rain came down (Genesis 7:11; Psalm 78:23); beneath the earth was mysterious Sheol where dwelt the shadowy dead (Isaiah 14:9–11); and all this had been made in six days, each of which had had a morning and an evening, a short and measurable time before (Genesis 1).

Are we to understand that this is Mr. Bryan's science, that we must teach this science in our schools, that we are es-

topped by divine revelation from ever going beyond this science? Yet this is exactly what Mr. Bryan would force us to if with intellectual consistency he should carry out the implications of his appeal to the Bible against the scientific hypothesis of evolution in biology.

The Bible's Precious Truths

One who is a teacher and preacher of religion raises his protest against all this just because it does such gross injustice to the Bible. There is no book to compare with it. The world never needed more its fundamental principles of life, its fully developed views of God and man, its finest faiths and hopes and loves. When one reads an article like Mr. Bryan's one feels, not that the Bible is being defended, but that it is being attacked. Is a 'cello defended when instead of being used for music it is advertised as a good dinner table? Mr. Bryan does a similar disservice to the Bible when, instead of using it for what it is, the most noble, useful, inspiring and inspired book of spiritual life which we have, the record of God's progressive unfolding of His character and will from early primitive beginnings to the high noon in Christ, he sets it up for what it is not and never was meant to be—a procrustean bed to whose infallible measurements all human thought must be forever trimmed.

The fundamental interest which leads Mr. Bryan and others of his school to hate evolution is the fear that it will depreciate the dignity of man. Just what do they mean? Even in the Book of Genesis God made man out of the dust of the earth. Surely, that is low enough to start and evolution starts no lower. So long as God is the creative power, what difference does it make whether out of the dust by sudden fiat or out of the dust by gradual process God brought man into being? Here man is and what he is he is. Were it decided that God had dropped him from the sky, he still would be the man he is. If it is decided that God brought him up by slow gradations out of lower forms of life, he still is the man he is.

The fact is that the process by which man came to be upon the planet is a very important scientific problem, but it is not a crucially important religious problem. Origins prove nothing in the realm of values. To all folk of spiritual insight man, no matter by what process he at first arrived, is the child of God, made in His image, destined for His character. If one could appeal directly to Mr. Bryan he would wish to say: let the scientists thresh out the problems of man's biological origin but in the meantime do not teach men that if God did not make us by fiat then we have nothing but a bestial heritage. That is a lie which once believed will have a terrific harvest. It is regrettable business that a prominent Christian should be teaching that.

One writes this with warm sympathy for the cause which gives Mr. Bryan such anxious concern. He is fearful that the youth of the new generation, taught the doctrine of a materialistic science, may lose that religious faith in God and in the realities of the spiritual life on which alone an abiding civilization can be founded. His fear is well grounded, as everyone closely associated with the students of our colleges and universities knows. Many of them are sadly confused, mentally in chaos, and, so far as any guiding principles of religious faith are concerned, are often without chart, compass or anchor.

Danger of Materialistic Teaching

There are types of teaching in our universities which are hostile to any confi-

dence in the creative reality of the spiritual life—dreary philosophies which reduce everything to predetermined mechanical activity. Some classrooms doubtless are, as Mr. Bryan thinks, antagonistic, in the effect which they produce, alike to sustained integrity of character, buoyancy and hopefulness of life and progress in society. But Mr. Bryan's association of this pessimistic and materialistic teaching with the biological theory of evolution is only drawing a red herring across the real trail. The distinction between inspiring, spiritually minded teachers and deadening, irreligious teachers is not at the point of belief in evolution at all. Our greatest teachers, as well as our poorest, those who are profoundly religious as well as those who are scornfully irreligious, believe in evolution. The new biology has no more to do with the difference between them than the new astronomy or the new chemistry. If the hypothesis of evolution were smashed tomorrow, there would be no more religiously minded scientists and no fewer irreligious ones.

Heart of Problem

The real crux of the problem in university circles is whether we are going to think of creative reality in physical or in spiritual terms, and that question cannot be met on the lines that Mr. Bryan has laid down. Indeed, the real enemies of the Christian faith, so far as our students are concerned, are not the evolutionary biologists, but folk like Mr. Bryan who insist on setting up artificial adhesions between Christianity and outgrown scientific opinions, and who proclaim that we cannot have one without the other. The pity is that so many students will believe him and, finding it impossible to retain the outgrown scientific opinions, will give up Christianity in accordance with Mr. Bryan's insistence that they must.

Quite as amazing as his view of the Bible is Mr. Bryan's view of the effect of evolution upon man's thought of God. If ever a topsy-turvy statement was made about any matter capable of definitive information, Mr. Bryan's statement deserves that description, for it turns the truth upside down. He says: "The theistic evolutionist puts God so far away that He ceases to be a present influence in the life. . . . Why should we want to imprison God in an impenetrable past? This is a living world. Why not a living God upon the throne? Why not allow Him to work now?" But the effect of evolution upon man's thought of God, as every serious student of theology knows, has been directly the opposite of what Mr. Bryan supposes. It was in the eighteenth century that men thought of God as the vague, dim figure over the crest of the first hill who gave this universal toboggan its primeval shove and has been watching it sliding ever since. It was in the eighteenth century that God was thought of as the absentee landlord who had built the house and left it—as the shipwright who had built the ship and then turned it over to the master mariners, his natural laws. Such ideas of God are associated with eighteenth century Deism, but the nineteenth century's most characteristic thought of God was in terms of immanence—God here in this world, the life of all that lives, the sustaining energy of all that exists, as our spirits are in our bodies, permeating, vitalizing, directing all.

The idea of evolution was one of the great factors in this most profitable change. In a world nailed together like a box, God, the Creator, had been thought of as a carpenter who created the universe long ago; now, in a world growing like a tree, ever more putting out new roots and new branches, God has more and more been seen as the indwelling spiritual life. Consider that bright light of nineteen-century Christianity, Henry Drummond, the companion of D. L. Moody in his evangelistic tours. He believed in evolution. What did it do to his thought of God? Just what it has done to the thought of multitudes. Said Drummond: "If God appears periodically He disappears periodically. If He comes upon the scene at special crises, He is absent from the scene in the intervals. Whether is all-God or occasional-God the nobler theory? Positively the idea of an immanent God, which is the God of evolution, is infinitely grander than the occasional wonder-worker who is the God of an old theology."

Mr. Bryan proposes, then, that instead of entering into this rich heritage where ancient faith, flowering out in new world views, grows richer with the passing centuries, we shall run ourselves into his mold of medievalism. He proposes, too, that his special form of medievalism shall be made authoritative by the state, promulgated as the only teaching allowed in the schools. Surely, we can promise him a long, long road to travel before he plunges the educational system of this country into such incredible folly, and if he does succeed in arousing a real battle over the issue we can promise him also that just as earnestly as the scientists will fight against him in the name of scientific freedom of investigation so will multitudes of Christians fight against him in the name of their religion and their God.

Arthur Garfield Hays: THE SCOPES TRIAL

THE sleepy town of Dayton, Tennessee, snuggled in the hills. Robinson's Drug Store was on the main street, a broad quiet village center flanked by the Aqua Hotel, a moving picture theater, a barber shop where one could get a hot bath, a livery stable and establishments of like character. George Rappelyea, a mining engineer, the live-wire of the town, Thomas Scopes, a young tow-headed High School teacher, and three lawyers, gathered in the drug store, discussed the Anti-Evolution law recently passed by the legislature. They read the wording of the Statute as printed in the Chattanooga *Times*:

"Be it enacted by the general assembly of the State of Tennessee that it shall be unlawful for any teacher in any of the universities, normals and all other public schools of the State, which are supported in whole or in part by the public school funds of the State, to teach any theory that denies the story of the Divine creation of man as taught in the Bible, and to teach instead that man has descended from a lower order of animals."

Suddenly Rappelyea pushed aside the paper and smote Mr. Robinson's glass-topped table.* Here was a chance to put Dayton on the map! Would Scopes agree to place himself and his munificent school-teaching job in jeopardy? Scopes would. Here was a magnificent opportunity to test an obnoxious law. The sensational character of the undertaking,

which would make Dayton world famous, was not an unwelcome feature. No time was to be lost. Other communities, once they caught the idea, would compete for the attraction of a trial involving science, the Bible and Tennessee. Scopes, a bit amused by it all, marched resignedly to the sacrifice. He intimated to his class that there might be something in the theory of evolution. He was arrested when his friends pointed out to the local constabulary just what he meant.

The stage was set. William Jennings Bryan, then resident in Florida, long a proponent of restrictive law to induce faith, and responsible more than any other for the Tennessee Statute, volunteered his services to the prosecution. Opportunity could grant no more. The exultant Rappelyea sent an S.O.S. for legal aid to the American Civil Liberties Union in New York. Clarence Darrow, Dudley Field Malone and myself answered the request to join Dr. John Randolph Neal, a lawyer of Tennessee, in the defense. The luster of Bainbridge Colby shone on us for a time, but he was unable to accompany us southward.

Scopes was indicted. The show was on. At once Dayton took on the character of a revivalist-circus. Thither swarmed ballyhoo artists, hot dog venders, lemonade merchants, preachers, professional atheists, college students, Greenwich Village radicals, out-of-work coal miners, I.W.W.'s, Single Taxers, "libertarians," revivalists of all shades and sects, hinterland "soothsayers," Holy Rollers, an

---

* The American Civil Liberties Union had announced that it would back any school teacher who would test the law.

From *Let Freedom Ring* by Arthur Garfield Hays. By permission of LIVERIGHT Publishers, Copyright 1955 Jane Butler, pp. 25–30, 37–39, 42–56, and 67–83.

army of newspaper men, scientists, editors and lawyers. Dayton, Tennessee, had found its place in the sun.

Tennessee and its people were surprising to an unsophisticated New York lawyer. When, on occasion, Europeans have talked about the United States, I have been amazed at their misunderstanding and sometimes at their credulity. I have expressed what I thought was the American point of view, with more or less the assumption that as an American I understood it. And yet, with wider experience I realize more and more that there is no American type—that different sections of the country and various groups of people hold such diverse views that they might well be living not only in different hemispheres but almost in different periods of civilization.

Within a few years prior to and during 1925, many states were considering laws prohibiting the teaching of evolution in the public schools. Some states had adopted this legislation in one form or another. The question of the propriety or constitutionality of such laws had not been tested. Dayton provided the test-tube. The case derived its interest not only from the subject matter but because the main antagonists were William Jennings Bryan and Clarence Darrow. It was a battle between two types of mind—the rigid, orthodox, accepting, unyielding, narrow, conventional mind, and the broad, liberal, critical, cynical, skeptical and tolerant mind.

On one occasion during the trial, Darrow turned to me and said: "Isn't it difficult to realize that a trial of this kind is possible in the Twentieth Century in the United States of America?" I should have been startled and somewhat doubtful had any one told me that at this late date there were great numbers of people in the United States who held the religious views of the Middle Ages, who, in spite of railroads, steamboats, the World War, the telephone, the airplane, the radio, all the great mechanistic discoveries and all the advancement in science and philosophy, in spite of education in the public schools in geography, biology and kindred subjects, still thought that the earth was flat; that doctors were a menace; that lawyers were predestined to damnation, and that failure to observe literally every word of the Bible would send one to eternal Hell, a material region where the flames leap high and where the doors are sealed for eternity. Had any one suggested that there were millions of people who believed it possible to build up a theocracy in the United States under the leadership of Bryan, I should have thought the statement that of a madman—that is, before I went to Dayton.

Bryan actually felt that this was a fight between religion and atheism or agnosticism. He never realized that it was a fight merely between a literal interpretation of the Bible and common sense. His attitude was no different from that of the Church for centuries. He rested religion upon the precise verbiage of the Book and insisted that religion would fail if those words were not accepted literally. Instead of accepting the spirit of religion or of Christianity, he accepted words, many of them the wrong words, many of them representing improper translations, all of them representing the ideas of men of thousands of years ago who spoke the language and expressed the ideas of their time. Such views lead to the downfall of religion, not to its growth. If to be religious one must believe things that his mind will not accept, he must, perforce, by human reasoning reject religion. Credulity may be a test of faith. It is not a test of rationality.

To the Fundamentalists faith is co-extensive with the Bible, the King James' version of the Bible. John Washington Butler, the farmer legislator who introduced the Tennessee Bill, is reported to have said that he never knew there was more than one Bible until he heard this stated in Court. Apparently he had never heard of the Catholic Bible consisting of eighty books, or the Hebrew Bible consisting of sixty-six books, or of any other translation. It is doubtful whether he ever inquired as to the language in which the original Bible was written, whether he knew that the Bible in Hebrew was unvocalized, and that changes in vowels might have brought about important changes in the text. Apparently he did not realize that, before the age of printing, many priests made their own translations and did not hesitate to change a meaning for their own purposes. In the Fifteenth Century in England a law was passed making it a death penalty to read the Bible in the original tongue; under this law thirty-nine men were hanged and their property confiscated to the Crown. Butler did not know that the stories of the Bible constitute the folk lore of many primitive peoples; that this is true of the story of the Creation, the flood, the Virgin birth and numerous other tales. If one had suggested that there had been no greater evolution than that of religion, and possibly that of the Bible itself, Butler would no doubt have stamped that person as an atheist and unbeliever. In fact, John W. Butler apparently thought, if indeed he thought at all, that the King James' version of the Bible was handed down by God in person to Moses, in printed form and in the English language. Any effort to enlighten Butler would have been met with the words of one of the attorneys for the prosecution, "If I must choose between religion and education, I choose religion." . . .

Of the jury as finally chosen, eleven were church members, one of whom did not go to church as often as he ought, the twelfth having slipped in by an oversight. The prosecution reexamined him when this curious fact appeared, but he had been accepted and there was no way to unseat him.

We made our motions on demurrer and to quash the indictment on constitutional grounds. The jury was dismissed during the argument although the constitution of the State of Tennessee states that in criminal cases the jury shall be the judge of the law as well as of the facts. We pointed out, among other things, that the Tennessee constitution provided that the caption of a bill should be germane to the substance, that the caption of this bill referred to the teaching of evolution, whereas the bill itself forbade the teaching of anything concerning Creation contrary to the Bible.

We then referred to a section of the State constitution which reads:

Knowledge, learning and virtue being essential to the preservation of republican institutions . . . it shall be the duty of the general assembly in all future periods of this Government to cherish literature and science.

A further provision is that "no preference shall ever be given by law to any religious establishment." When we suggested that this was violated by a law favoring the Fundamentalists, the answer of the Attorney General was, "Oh, that is all foolishness."

We contended that under the Fourteenth Amendment to the United States Constitution, no law was sound which was so indefinite that one could not tell what was forbidden, that no man could be in a position where he might "guess" himself into jail. In the first place, the act referred to the theory of Creation as set forth in the Bible. There is no statement of what Bible is intended. Then, there are various stories of Creation in the Bible. Is the test based on the Bible literally interpreted? The word "teach" leads to further difficulty. Does it mean teach "as a fact" or does it mean "to expound information"? For, obviously, if it doesn't mean to teach as a fact, then one may teach, or expound information, on all theories.

We made the further contention that the law did not come within the police power of the State. The liberty of the individual can be limited by the State only under the police power. No law which is unreasonable can be justified by the police power. As a test, we presented a parallel law that it should be unlawful for any one to teach in the public schools any theory contrary to the Bible that the earth is not the center of the universe, and to teach instead thereof that the earth moves around the sun. We suggested the death penalty for violation. We insisted that the only difference between the supposititious law and the one in question was that the scientific fact of the earth's movement was to-day accepted. We thought the illustration was far-fetched but back in the hills of Tennessee is a sect called the Holy Rollers who would regard such legislation not only with favor but who would feel that it represented the word of God. Yet I have never observed more sincere and deeply religious people than the Holy Rollers. . . .

Our argument, ridiculing the law, aroused General McKenzie, the old war horse of the Tennessee Bar. He insisted that any boy of sixteen knows all about evolution and also about the Bible, i.e.,

any boy of sixteen born and raised in Tennessee. In reference to our hypothetical act he said, "No such act as that has ever passed through the fertile brain of a Tennesseean. I don't know what they do up in their country." Malone objected to allusions to geographical location and suggested that we were there as American citizens. The Court tried to smooth the troubled waters by suggesting that General McKenzie loved us all and that we should always remember that we were guests. Mr. Malone answered with some asperity that in the courtroom we were lawyers and not guests.

The argument for the law was simple and persuasive. The public owned the schools and paid the teachers. The public had a right to direct what the teacher should say or do. The teacher is their employee. Certainly the people should not be compelled to hire and pay a teacher to destroy the faith of their children. The agnostic insists that the public supply not only the schools and the teachers but even the pupils, and demands the right to teach doctrines of which the people disapprove. Appallingly unjust! Those who in New York State approved the infamous Lusk laws will have no difficulty with the reasoning.

Of course, the answer is that the State may determine what subjects shall be taught, but if biology is to be taught, it cannot demand that it be taught falsely. If astronomy is to be taught, the State could not legislate that no one teach that the earth moves around the sun; if geography, that the earth is round; if arithmetic, that two and two make four. The State may decide that physiology should not be taught. If, however, that is a prescribed subject, the State could hardly provide by law that children be taught that men and women have all of the same physical characteristics.

Sue Hicks, a young Tennessee lawyer, assured the court that our contentions were ridiculous, that the prosecution failed to see that there was any religious issue whatever involved, and that certainly the act in no way interfered with the promotion of science and learning. Personally, I doubt whether at any time the attorneys for the prosecution caught our point on the religious question. Every word, to say nothing of emotions, in the court made it clear that there was really no other question. The constitution provided against preference to any religious establishment. We insisted that the Fundamentalist Church was a religious establishment and that preference was given to Fundamentalists by making their Bible, and their interpretation of the Bible, the yardstick of education. When General Stewart asked how the law interfered with the constitution, Mr. Darrow answered, "Giving preference to the Bible." General Stewart replied, "To the Bible?" Mr. Darrow: "Yes, sir. Yes, over the Koran." General Stewart: "What is there in this that requires you to worship in any particular way?" But we insisted that the law preferred the Bible to the Koran. The Koran was not popular in the State of Tennessee.

It then appeared that the State of Tennessee prescribed the textbook from which Scopes had taught. For Scopes to have used any other textbook would have been a misdemeanor, and yet it was likewise a crime for him to have used this.

Then rose the well beloved and well hated Darrow, tall with stooped shoulders, lined face, lanky figure, in shirtsleeves and lavender suspenders. At times he spoke in soft tones, then sardonic, then indignant. He started quietly, pointing out casually that while we came from Chicago and New York, yet Mr. Bryan, Sr., a foreigner, from Florida, and

Mr. Bryan, Jr., from California, were responsible for this "foolish, mischievous and wicked act." He quoted the statement of Bancroft that "it is all right to preserve freedom in constitutions, but when the spirit of freedom has fled from the hearts of the people, then its matter is easily sacrificed under law."

Here we find to-day as brazen and as bold an attempt to destroy learning as was ever made in the Middle Ages and the only difference is we have not provided that malefactors shall be burned at the stake. But there is time for that, your Honor. We have to approach these things gradually.

He pointed out that the State of Tennessee "has no more right to teach the Bible as the Divine Book than the Book of Mormon or the Book of Confucius or the Essays of Emerson or any one of the ten thousand books to which human souls have gone for consolation and aid in their troubles." Again he referred to the statute as indefinite; nobody could tell what it meant, it might be a trap to get some one who did not agree with you.

Does this statute state what you shall teach and what you shall not? Not at all. Does it say that you cannot teach that the earth is round because Genesis says that it is flat? No. Does it say that you cannot teach that the earth is millions of ages old because the account in Genesis makes it less than six thousand years old? Oh, no. It does not state that. If it did you could understand it. It says you shan't teach any theory of the origin of man that is contrary to the Divine theory contained in the Bible.

It makes the Bible the yardstick to measure every man's intelligence and to measure every man's learning. Are your mathematics good? Turn to Elijah i:2. Is your philosophy good? See II Samuel 3. Is your astronomy good? See Genesis, Chapter ii, verse 7. Is your chemistry good? See—well, chemistry, see Deuteronomy 6, or anything that tells about brimstone. Every bit of knowledge that the mind has must be submitted to a religious test.

(A later check-up showed that Darrow's verse references were not accurate, but this did not detract from the argument.) Finally, in a burst of fire and eloquence came the peroration:

If to-day you can take a thing like evolution and make it a crime to teach it in the public school . . . at the next session you may ban books and newspapers. Soon you may set Catholic against Protestant, and Protestant against Protestant. . . . Ignorance and fanaticism are ever busy and need feeding. Always they are anxious and gloating for more. . . .

After awhile, your Honor, it is the setting of man against man and creed against creed until with flying banners and beating drums we are marching backward to the glorious ages of the Sixteenth Century when bigots lighted fagots to burn the men who dared to bring any intelligence and enlightenment and culture to the human mind.

This was the high spot of the day and the message went flying throughout the country.

That night the water supply of Dayton did not function, and the electric lights were not working. Next morning, the denizens commented, with furtive looks Darrow-ward, upon the miracle that the water had ceased to flow, the lights had ceased to burn, and some suggested that the rivers flowed with blood!

We looked upon the day's work and found it good. There was morning and there was evening that day and a ray of light had been flashed in Tennessee.

We have alluded to the fact that proceedings in court opened with prayer. We did not object to this until the second day. Then we quietly asked the

Judge to dispense with this amazing procedure, claiming that it was conceivable that it might prejudice the jury. This having had no effect, we made our objection in open court. Now, the idea that prayer should not be indulged in, any time, any place, under any circumstances, was extremely novel to Dayton, Tennessee, and a gasp of shocked awe went through the courtroom. General Stewart referred to the agnostic counsel for the defense. Mr. Malone objected that we had heard prayers daily; that they were "argumentative and helped to increase the atmosphere of hostility," to which General Stewart retorted that he would advise Mr. Malone "that this is a God-fearing country." The court finally stated that he was "pleased to overrule the objection" and Dr. Stribling thereupon prayed that all of us be blessed.

We waited for a decision of the court on the demurrer and the motion to quash the indictment, but Judge Raulston stated that "he had not worked last night; that the lights were out until 8:30. . . ." Thereupon the court adjourned until the afternoon session. A petition was then presented from Unitarians, Jews and Congregationalists, that if prayer was to be said, there be a selection of clergymen to include others than Fundamentalists and a motion was made that the petition be granted. The decision on the motion was referred by the court to the "Pastors' Association of this town." We objected that we were entitled to a judicial determination of the motion, but the court held to its ruling.

Still we awaited the court's opinion on the constitutionality of the law, but Judge Raulston remarked that he "had a very serious matter to speak of"; that he had been informed that newspapers had already published his decision; that no one except his secretary and himself knew his conclusion, and that before reading his momentous opinion he intended to conduct an investigation to find out how there had come a leak of the news. Thereupon one of the reporters suggested to the Judge that the way to go about the matter was to appoint a committee of newspaper men to look into the matter. A list of proposed members was handed to the Judge, who promptly appointed the nominees. It was generally known that the "scoop" had been made by a youngster named Hutchinson, representing the International News Service, but in the evening the Committee, with great hilarity and some disregard for the Volstead Act, held a mock trial. They reported to court that Hutchinson had come by his information in a legitimate manner. The court insisted upon knowing the source. Whereupon, Mr. Beemish, the chairman, remarked, "Upon investigation we find that the information came from the court." Judge Raulston interjected a startled, "What?" Whereupon Mr. Beemish continued: Hutchinson had met the Judge the day before upon his way to the hotel. The Judge had said that a stenographer was making a copy of the decision. He was asked whether he would read the decision in the afternoon, to which the Judge's answer was that such was his intention. The next question was whether the court would adjourn until to-morrow, to which the reply was, "Yes, I think so." The inference was clear. If the motion to quash was granted, the trial would be at an end. An adjournment meant the denial of the motion. Hutchinson drew the obvious deduction. Whereupon the court with great dignity delivered a homily to these hard-boiled reporters, stars of the profession, drawn from all over the country. He informed them that he did not

expect them to ask him questions without giving him direct notice of the purpose of the inquiry and that to draw deductions seemed to him to be a scurrilous betrayal of the hospitality of the South.

We were impatient for the court's opinion, but the question of prayer was still dominant. Our associate, Neal, insisted that the court should take judicial notice of the fact that the people of the world were divided into numerous sects and that we differed from the Attorney General in his statement that the case did not involve a religious question. This aroused Sue Hicks. "I have set over here and remained quiet these three days," he said, but on behalf of the court he wished to point out that during a period of five years every time he had been in a court where a minister had happened to stray, proceedings were opened with prayer. He wanted to know why we objected to prayer if evolution did not contradict the Bible. The Judge explained that he had had no purpose "to influence anybody wrongfully" and hoped that prayer might "influence somebody rightfully. . . . I do not think it hurts anybody and I think it may help somebody."

The next order of business was a request by General Stewart to be permitted to apologize for rude words to myself in court the day before. He was permitted. He apologized. Thereupon Neal insisted that Stewart likewise apologize to Mr. Darrow for having called him an "infidel" and "agnostic." Stewart replied, "So long as I speak what I conceive to be the truth I apologize to no man." (Loud applause from the audience.)

Darrow explained that he did not except to General Stewart's statement: that as to the word "agnostic" he was proud to admit that he knew nothing of subjects on which so very many ignorant men were sure. As to the word "infidel" Darrow insisted it had no meaning whatever; that everybody is an infidel who does not believe in the prevailing religion. "Among the Saracens," he continued blandly, "everybody is an infidel who does not believe with them. In a Mohammedan country everybody is an infidel that does not believe with them, and among Christians everybody is an infidel that is not a Christian, or at least does not profess to be." Further, Darrow added that he hated to be accused of such a foolish thing as infidelity, because everybody at some time or another is guilty of that. The court asked General Stewart what he thought of this. Stewart answered that he thought "we were wasting a lot of valuable time."

This debris having been cleared away, Judge Raulston was ready to read his opinion. He requested order and turning to the photographers said, "If you gentlemen want to make my picture, make it now."

The motion to quash was overruled; the demurrer was denied.

The jury was then called in. Several days had passed. We were now about ready to proceed with the evidence. A newspaper reporter, however, interrupted: "Can we have chairs, Judge?" The court: "Gentlemen, I don't believe the whole courtroom should expect the Judge should look after chairs. Let the Sheriff do that, appeal to the Sheriff." General McKenzie objected that people carried off the chairs of the attorneys and remarked that "we are a necessary evil in the courtroom." The sheriff announced that no chairs should be purloined from attorneys or from the press. Juror Thompson then requested electric fans, "if it ain't out of order."

General Stewart opened for the prosecution, Malone for the defense. Dudley Field Malone, one-time darling of the Democratic party, a former aide of Bryan—Malone, spruce and well-groomed from his trim shoes to his unwrinkled soft silk collar even in the heat of Dayton, rose to speak. The newspaper men remarked upon his well-fitting Metropolitan shirts. They were made in England. Mine came from the same shop, but they received no public commendation: "Hays was thick-set, stocky, democratic-looking, with rough shirt, open at the neck."

Malone did not proceed far without interruption. General McKenzie objected to the explanation of the defense case to the jury, insisting that Malone could not discuss evolution or the Bible, since the only question in the case was whether man was descended from a lower order of animals. For Malone to discuss other issues, said McKenzie, "would be like a couple of gentlemen over in my country where they were engaged in a lawsuit before a Justice of the Peace. There were a large number of witnesses. Finally, after conference, the lawyers came back and one of them reported 'if your Honor please, the witnesses in this case, some of them are not very well and others are awfully ignorant, and we have just agreed among ourselves to dispense with the evidence and argue the case.'" General McKenzie informed Malone that "the only mistake the good Lord made is that he did not withhold the completion of the job until he consulted you." Mr. Malone: "I rather think you are right."

The witnesses were sworn. Little boys in short trousers, girls in pinafores, all brightly polished for the occasion, the school superintendent and other leading members of Dayton's intelligentsia stood on one side. On the other, Maynard Metcalf of Johns Hopkins, Kirtley F. Mather of Harvard, Wilbur Nelson, State Geologist, Dr. Jacob Lippman, Winterton C. Curtis, Charles Hubbard Judd, Fay Cooper Cole, Horatio H. Newman, and others of the most eminent scientists of the day.

Walter White, school superintendent, testified that Scopes had used the book "Hunter's Civil Biology." Scopes had said that he could not teach the book without teaching the part pertaining to evolution.

The prosecution offered in evidence and asked the court to take judicial notice of the King James' version of the Bible. Objection was made on the ground that the King James' Bible could not be accepted in evidence unless some witness was ready to testify that that was *the* Bible. We pointed out that there was the Douay version of the Bible used by the Catholics, and the Hebrew Bible; that the original manuscripts, in Hebrew, Aramaic and Greek, had been lost for hundreds of years, and that all one had to-day were translations of translations; that the earliest copy of the Old Testament in Hebrew now in existence was made in the Eleventh Century, although there were partial copies made in the Ninth and Tenth Centuries; that the oldest Greek manuscripts, except a few fragments, belonged to the Fourth and Fifth Centuries. Each part claims its own version to be inspired. We argued that the statute did not refer to the King James' version. There was no law under which the court could take judicial notice of that or any other version in a case which involved *the* Bible.

THE COURT: Mr. Hays, would you raise the same objection if they attempted to file any other Bible?

MR. HAYS: Not if some one testified that the King James' or any other version is *the* Bible; then the jury could believe or disbelieve the statement.

THE COURT: Let your objection be overruled. Let it be introduced as *the* Bible.

Howard Morgan, a cleancut youngster of about fourteen, thereupon testified that he was in Scopes' class and that Scopes taught the following:

"He said that the earth was once a hot molten mass, too hot for plant or animal life to exist upon it; in the sea the earth cooled off; there was a little germ of one cell organism formed, and this organism kept evolving until it got to be a land animal, and it kept on evolving, and from this was man."

Scopes also had classified man as a "mammal." Darrow took up the cross-examination:

Q. Now, Howard, what do you mean by "classify"?

A. Well, it means classify these animals we mentioned, that men were just the same as them.

Q. In other words, he did not say a cat was the same as a man?

A. No, sir; that man had reasoning power, that these animals did not.

Q. There is some doubt about that, but that is what he said, is it?

Darrow inquired whether Scopes had not taught that mammals were animals that had hair and suckled their young, and that among them were dogs and horses, monkeys, cows, man and whales.

A. Yes, sir; but I don't know about the whales. He said all those other ones.

Q. Well, did he tell you anything else that was wicked?

A. No, not that I remember of.

Darrow asked benevolently about the development of life, the teaching that the first life was in the sea; that it developed into life on the land and finally into the organism known as man. And then to Howard, "It has not hurt you any, has it?" A. "No, sir." The witness testified that there was nothing in the book that said that man was descended from monkey, not that he "knew of."

The next day Bryan arose and absolutely and unequivocally refused to be a mammal. Other people could do about it as they pleased, but as for him, he would have none of it. He pointed out a diagram in this corrupting textbook classifying animals beginning with the protozoa—indicating different varieties in separate species—protozoa, sponges, insects, fishes, amphibia, reptiles, birds and mammals, some 3,500 of them, "and among them," said Bryan, "is man. They left him there with 3,499 other mammals, among them skunks and other animals that smell bad. They have an odor that extends beyond the circumference of this circle." No, Bryan would not admit he was a mammal. One of the newspaper wags afterwards pointed out that according to Darrow's test, perhaps Bryan was right, for he neither had hair nor did he suckle his young.

Bryan protested further. According to the scientists, man was not even descended from American monkeys, but from Old World monkeys. In order to make his argument clear, Bryan dragged in the famous Leopold-Loeb case, quoting the words of Darrow that children were the product of their environment. Darrow objected. The court asked on what ground. Darrow said this was obviously intended to create prejudice. Mr. Bryan denied this, whereupon Darrow interjected: "What's the use of it then?"

Dr. Maynard M. Metcalf, witness for the defense, took the stand. Objection was made to his testimony on the ground that the theory of evolution had nothing to do with the case. We were permitted, however, to examine him in order to raise the question of the materiality of the evidence. As Dr. Metcalf testified to some of the wonders of science, giving a modest guess of the age of the earth at six hundred million years, as he traced through the countless ages the development of life on earth, the crowd in the courtroom, awed and silent, listened tensely to the words of science which they feared might upset their faith. He explained that "evolution and the theories of evolution are fundamentally different things. The fact of evolution is . . . perfectly and absolutely clear. There are dozens of theories . . . as to the methods by which evolution has been brought about . . . The term evolution in general means the whole series of changes which have taken place during hundreds of millions of years which have produced from lowly beginnings . . . organisms of much more complex character."

The statements of various scientists sought to clear up the misunderstanding as to what evolution is. It was "the most satisfactory explanation of the observed facts relating to the universe, to our world and all life on it" or "a great scientific generalization, the only relational explanation of an overwhelming mass of facts."

Then we settled down to tell the story of evolution in as bizarre and breathtaking a setting as that amazing story has ever had. . . .

The following day the court promptly held that the scientific evidence was not admissible. An exception was noted on the ground that "for the Court of Rhea County to try to determine whether or not this law is unreasonable without informing itself by evidence, assumed plenary knowledge of matters which have been the subject of study of scientists for generations."

Mr. Bryan then insisted that he wished to cross-examine the witnesses whose statements had been read into the record. Our objection was based on rather an interesting reason. While, if the testimony had been admitted, cross-examination would of course have followed, yet we had merely presented the statements to show what testimony we could have adduced. Cross-examination would have shown that the scientists, while religious men—for we chose only that kind— still did not believe in the Virgin birth and other miracles. It was felt by us that if the cause of free education was ever to be won, it would need the support of millions of intelligent churchgoing people who didn't question theological miracles.

Then occurred the interesting colloquy for which Darrow was cited for contempt. The court asked the purpose of cross-examination, to which Darrow responded, "to create prejudice, your Honor." The court reminded Darrow that he must always expect the court to rule correctly, whereupon Darrow said that we were taking our exceptions in order to protect our rights in some other tribunal, adding, "Now, that is plain enough, isn't it?"

THE COURT: I hope you don't think the court is trying to be unfair. To which Darrow, hitching up one suspender strap, drawled out the caustic retort, "Your Honor has the right to hope." A prolonged but electric silence ensued. The hearing was adjourned.

During the week-end the atmosphere seethed with excitement. The Tennesseeans have considerable regard for the dignity of the court. It was felt that Darrow's remarks had been willfully contemptuous. On the one hand respect for

the court seemed to demand that something be done about it. But there was the haunting fear that if Darrow were cited for contempt the court might have to punish him. Darrow in jail would be a fearful antagonist. The case was sufficiently dramatic without adding dynamite. Darrow had intended to apologize but learning that the court wished to take action, felt that he should wait.

On Monday, at the opening of court, the Judge read aloud his version of the occurrence. When the matter appeared in consecutive fashion, it seemed to us of the defense even more satisfactory than did the original colloquy. Darrow was cited for contempt and was held, pending the return of the citation, under bond of $5,000.

Later in the day Darrow rendered his apology. The purport was that whatever a lawyer might think of a judge as an individual, or of his acts or decisions, yet, as a member of the bar, he should never fail to show respect for the institution of the court. The apology was accepted. Judge Raulston showed mercy. He gazed benignly upon Mr. Darrow and spoke solemnly: "The Man that I believe came into the world to save man from sin, the Man that died on the cross that man might be redeemed, taught that it was godly to forgive . . . the Saviour died on the cross pleading with God for the men who crucified Him. I believe in that Christ. I believe in these principles. I accept Colonel Darrow's apology. . . . We commend him to go back home and learn in his heart the words of the Man who said, 'If ye thirst come unto me and I will give thee life.'"

The defense offered in evidence the message of Governor Peay approving the anti-evolution bill. There was intimation here that probably the law would never be enforced. Then we offered a new textbook called "Biology and Human Welfare," by Peabody & Hunt, recently adopted by the State Commission. This book referred to Darwin, also to mammals. It was contended that all of this threw light on the public policy of the State.

Thousands of people had come to court to listen to the summation of the case. The room was jammed. There was some question about its safety. A rough platform had been erected next to the courthouse, and proceedings were adjourned to the courtyard. On one side of the platform were the attorneys for the defense; on the other, the prosecution; in the middle, the Judge's bench. Below, under the spreading trees, was the audience. And what an audience! In the front row the newspaper men sitting on the bare ground and scribbling furiously away, using knees, platform props and the shoulders of their neighbors for copypaper rests. On one side were adherents of Darrow, youngsters for the most part (some from the vicinity, some from far away who had hitchhiked the distance). Now and then Darrow would glance down at them over his spectacles, as if drawing strength from his supporters. And on the other side of the square, beneath the platform, were the Bryanites, gnarled farmers, their brows knit with the struggle of following the swift battle of the giants; tight-lipped women with weary lines of drudgery around their eyes, confused but confident that Righteousness would prevail; stern-visaged Men of God, some of them clothed in stifling broadcloth beneath a pitiless Tennessee sun, which shone alike on believers and skeptics.

The jury was called to the box. Another quarrel arose over a side issue. Fronting the twelve good men and true, was a sign about ten feet long: "Read your Bible." We objected. The prosecution protested our disrespect. Discussion was long and heated. The sign was removed. Tennessee farmers were shocked. The case proceeded. The defense offered in evidence a Catholic Bible. The court asked whether it was in English. The court accepted it. The Tennessee farmers were stunned. A Catholic Bible and on the Judge's bench! Judge Raulston, after a little cautious scanning, remarked that the story of Genesis there was not very different. We contended that if any word differed from the King James' version, we could argue to the jury that the Bible was a man-made, not a God-made, document. Then was offered a Hebrew Bible, not in English. This was accepted. But to our surprise we were not permitted to call a witness to translate the story of Genesis. The Judge was wiser than he knew.

To the Mansion—the euphonious name for the ramshackle dwelling which we of the defense occupied—Rabbi Herman Rosenwasser of San Francisco had brought a chart of Hebrew characters. It was the story of Genesis. Night after night he conducted a class made up of the assembled body of scientists and lawyers. His method was as follows: He would translate the Hebrew into German and we had a choice of perhaps six German words for each Hebrew word. He then translated the German into English and we had a choice of perhaps six English words for every German word. By the time we got through we could make Genesis say pretty nearly what we wanted. Thus, God did not "create" the earth—he "evolved" it, or "set it in motion," which would do quite as well. The words in Psalms, usually rendered, "He hath made a decree which shall not pass," are properly translated, "He hath made a law of nature which He doth not transgress." Our new translation would have startled the faithful.

In response to a query as to whether the defense had any more evidence to offer, I stated that we wished to call Mr. Bryan as an expert on the Bible. I have never yet discovered whether this was a greater surprise to Darrow or to Bryan. Darrow turned to Malone: "You examine him, Dudley." Malone answered, "Oh no." Darrow turned to me. I shook my head.

Then came the battle that was the quintessence of the whole case. Perhaps never before in the history of the world has a witness under cross-examination attempted rationally to defend beliefs not based on rational reasoning.

Bryan took the stand conditionally. "If your Honor please, I insist that Mr. Darrow be put on the stand, and Mr. Malone and Mr. Hays."

THE COURT: Call anybody you desire. Ask him any questions you wish.

MR. BRYAN: Then we will call all three of them.

Darrow started in. Slouching back in his chair at first, later on shooting forward as he hammered a question home across the deal table that separated him from his famous antagonist, Darrow, reading from the Bible on his knee, looked like a benign Sunday-school superintendent, a bit *déshabillé* perhaps, lecturing a class on a hot Sabbath afternoon. Bryan assured him that he accepted the Bible literally; that he believed that a whale swallowed Jonah, although Bryan thought it was a fish rather than a whale. Darrow asked whether this was a "mine" run of fish or made specially for the purpose. Bryan was not prepared to say. When he was asked whether the Lord purposefully made a fish big enough to swallow Jonah, he answered affirmatively, adding,

"One miracle is just as easy for me to believe as another," to which Darrow responded, "It is for me too." When asked whether he thought that Joshua had made the sun stand still, Bryan replied that he accepted the Bible literally. Bryan had never pondered what would have happened to the earth had the sun stood still; the God he believed in would have taken care of that.

DARROW: Don't you know it would have been converted into a molten mass of matter?

BRYAN: You testify to that when you get on the stand. I will give you a chance.

DARROW: You have never investigated that subject?

BRYAN: I don't think I have ever had the question asked.

DARROW: Or ever thought of it?

BRYAN: I have been too busy on things that I thought were of more importance than that.

Bryan thought the world was created in 4004 B.C., the date appearing in the King James' version of the Bible. The calculation was made by Bishop Ussher who figured it out from the ages of the prophets. Ussher fixed the time more definitely. According to the Bishop, the year was not only 4004 B.C. but the date was the 23rd day of October, and at nine o'clock in the morning, to which some infidel voice in the audience added, "Eastern Standard Time." Darrow inquired how long ago the flood occurred. Bryan, cautious, first wished to see Ussher's calculations. From this he figured the date as 2348 B.C.

DARROW: When was that flood?

BRYAN: I would not attempt to fix the date. The date is fixed as suggested this morning.

DARROW: But what do you think that the Bible, itself, says? Don't you know how it was arrived at?

BRYAN: I never made a calculation.

DARROW: A calculation from what?

BRYAN: I could not say.

DARROW: What do you think?

BRYAN: I do not think about things I don't think about.

DARROW: Do you think about things you do think about?

BRYAN: Well, sometimes.

No evidence had ever satisfied Bryan that there was any civilization more than 5,000 years old. He believed that the human race did not run back more than 4,300 years. He did not know whether any scientist would agree with him but he was not sure that the matter was important. On one occasion when the crowd applauded, Bryan turned to Darrow: "And these are the people you call yokels," to which Darrow responded, "Those who are applauding you, I do call yokels." Bryan traced all language back to the fall of the Tower of Babel somewhere around 2218 B.C., never having seen any evidence that would persuade him that languages had developed otherwise. He had never studied philology. Bryan was sure that the world was created in six days, but not that these were 24-hour days. That was helpful to our case for if a Fundamentalist concedes anything to interpretation, he concedes his whole case.

As the drama developed, the amazing chorus below the actors sighed and groaned, laughed and grumbled, "hurrahed" or "amened" in alternate triumph or despair.

Continually Mr. Stewart objected to the examination, calling it a harangue. Mr. Bryan bravely insisted upon proceeding, stating that he was simply try-

ing "to protect the word of God against the greatest atheist or agnostic in the United States,"—a statement which brought loud applause. Bryan believed that the first woman was Eve; that she was actually and literally made out of Adam's rib. When asked if he had ever discovered where Cain got his wife, he answered sharply: "I leave the agnostics to hunt for her." He did not know whether there were other people on earth at that time. He believed the sun was made on the fourth day and that there was evening and morning without the sun. Yet creation might have gone on for a long time—millions of years—for a day is to the Lord as a thousand years. He believed the story of the temptation of Eve by the serpent and that all the troubles of man arose from that little *contretemps* in the Garden of Eden. Women suffered torture in childbirth because of Eve's dereliction, which reminds one that when opiates were first known objection was made to their use until some one reminded the theologians that God put Adam to sleep before he removed his rib. Bryan was asked whether he thought that God had made the serpent crawl on his belly because of his participation in the temptation. He did. "How do you suppose the snake got along before that?" queried Darrow.

The day ended with Bryan protesting that the only purpose Mr. Darrow has is to slur at the Bible. . . . I want the world to know that this man, who does not believe in a God, is trying to use a court in Tennessee—

DARROW: I object to that.

BRYAN: to slur at it. . . .

DARROW: I object to your statement. I am examining you on your fool ideas that no intelligent Christian on earth believes.

THE COURT: Court is adjourned until nine o'clock tomorrow morning.

The examination, starting calmly, had grown in tensity. At times Darrow and Bryan rose and glowered at each other, shaking their fists. There were constant interruptions by State Counsel, General McKenzie once stating that we would "no more file the testimony of Colonel Bryan as a part of the record than they would file a rattlesnake and handle it themselves." In unison we shouted, "We will file it. We will file it. File every word of it." But we didn't. The Supreme Court of Tennessee attended to that.[1]

This was the evening of the seventh day.

Several times there was cheering from one side or the other and when at last it was over, the followers of Darrow rose up and swarmed on the platform, keen to seize the hand of their champion.

Few came to Bryan. The man who, up to then, had everywhere been followed as a conquering hero, stood apart, almost alone, a strange tired expression on his face as he looked into the twilight that was closing all about him. One could not but feel a deep pity for the fallen Commoner.

Much had been accomplished by this examination. Bryan had conceded that he interpreted the Bible in at least one respect. He must have agreed that others have that right. We had expected to force Bryan to admit that there was nothing in the Bible contrary to evolution. In fact, much can be found to support that theory—which should not be surprising—since almost all causes, however contradictory, can find support.

At one point, Stewart, in objecting, had expostulated that the examination

[1] John Thomas Scopes vs. The State of Tennessee, 152 Tenn. 424 (1926)

"is not worth anything to them, if your Honor please, even for the record in the Supreme Court"; to which we answered, "Is it not worth something to us on the Story of Creation, if Mr. Bryan, as a Bible student, agrees that you cannot take the Bible as literally true?" Stewart: "The Bible speaks for itself." "But," we countered, "do you mean to say the Bible itself tells whether these are parables? Does it?"

When, on the morning of the eighth day we appeared in Court ready to continue the examination, the Judge not only refused to permit us to proceed, but stated that he was "pleased to expunge this testimony, given by Mr. Bryan on yesterday, from the records of this Court, and it will not be further considered."

Since, according to the interpretation of the Court, the only question in the case was whether Scopes had taught that man was descended from a "lower order of animals," a fact that was conceded from the beginning, we were ready for the verdict of the jury. These involuntary exiles were called in. Indignant at their regular exclusion from the courtroom, many of them would have voted to acquit Scopes had there been the slightest loophole. Darrow told the men of the jury that he was glad to see them, that he had missed them during the trial; that he hoped that nobody would stand out against a verdict of guilty because that would interfere with our appeal.

The Court instructed the jury. There was some discussion about the amount of the fine, which under the Tennessee Constitution is fixed by the jury. It appeared that the usual fine for transporting liquor was $100, and it was suggested that there should be no greater fine for transporting information. The

Court told the jury that if they wished to assess the minimum fine, this would be implied merely by a verdict "guilty" without naming a figure. The Court would then impose a minimum as "that is our practice in whisky cases." Darrow said we did not care who named the fine, that we would not take an exception either way. The matter later turned out to be of vital consequence.

Scopes was found guilty. Before judgment was pronounced he stood before the Judge and said calmly:

"Your Honor, I feel that I have been convicted for violation of an unjust statute. I will continue in the future, as I have in the past, to oppose this law in any way I can. Any other action would be in violation of my ideal of academic freedom."

Many, including a Canadian newspaper correspondent, made speeches of felicitation; the Court itself made a little oration, referring among other things to the fact that "truth crushed to earth will rise again." I asked his Honor to permit me to send him a copy of Darwin's "Descent of Man" and "Origin of Species." I came back from Tennessee with a copy of the Bible. When the Court reads Darwin, he will discount every scientific statement in it. I shall do the same with the Bible.

Within a few days of the trial, William Jennings Bryan died. Had this happened to Darrow, Tennessee would have regarded it as a judgment of God. As it was, Bryan was gathered to the angels. Inquiry is often made as to the effect of the trial on him. Did he die from age, disease, disappointment or over-eating? It is a moot question. No doubt he was much upset. His first entry into the courtroom was greeted with applause; his every word in debate was accepted as from a prophet. Then came the re-

vealing encounter with Darrow. Probably he himself never realized the depth of his humiliation, for he had had the support of a large quantity, and rather a fair quality, of ignorance and bigotry, but undoubtedly he was chagrined.

The youngsters of the Dayton High School gave a dance in honor of Clarence Darrow. He attended, danced and even smoked cigarettes with them. They seemed to recognize that this was their battle; that, although perhaps fought on different lines, it represented the issue between the eagerness of youth and the fear of age. Any pleasure, unconnected with the church, had been condemned by their elders. Smoking, dancing, free association between girls and boys, games and movies on Sunday had been their issues at home. Here were champions indeed. And we of the defense seemed to enjoy some popularity in Dayton. We "mixed" more than the Bryanites. And when the boys came to us from the telegraph office, they received liberal tips. A dollar gratuity in Dayton was widely heralded by the recipient, and not wholly disapproved by the denizens.

Argument on the appeal was heard in June, 1926. Tennessee lawyers, at first hesitant, flocked to our standard. Robert Keebler of Memphis, and John R. Neal of Knoxville, had been with us from the beginning, but we were joined by other leaders of the bar, among them, Thomas Malone and Edward E. Colton of Nashville. Our arguments in the court below were developed on appeal, but our local associates laid particular stress upon the indefiniteness of the law. This would give the court a way out. A decision on that ground would not offend public sensibilities.

Argument before the Supreme Court was in a far different atmosphere from that of the trial. Everything was calm, dignified and quiet, though intense. Bryan had passed away, public interest had largely subsided, Tennessee resented the world-wide ridicule the case had aroused.

As was expected, the court disregarded the contentions concerning religious preferences and the police power of the State. It dealt chiefly with the question of the indefiniteness of the law. Two judges, in a prevailing opinion, held that the law was definite. A third judge, concurring in the opinion, likewise held that the law was definite but interpreted it quite differently from the other two and to the effect that the law merely prohibited the teaching of materialistic theory. The fourth judge dissented on the ground that the law was indefinite and thus unconstitutional. Had the court rested there, we should have been well satisfied. We should then have appealed to the Supreme Court of the United States, our final goal. But the decision was a subtle one. Determined to prevent an appeal, the court, having decided that the law was constitutional, nevertheless reversed the conviction on the ground that the fine had been improperly imposed by the judge, a question not raised on appeal and on which no exception had been taken. And this, in spite of the fact that, in prior cases which arose in connection with fines for violation of the liquor laws, the Supreme Court had justified the imposition of a fine by the presiding judge where the minimum had been imposed.

The court did more than this. It not only reversed the verdict, but it also directed the Attorney General to *nolle prosse* all proceedings in this "bizarre" case, thus practically agreeing with Governor Peay in his message accompanying the passage of the law that it was a statute which was not to be enforced. For obviously, if the Supreme Court disapproved enforcement against Scopes or prosecution of Scopes as a violator, it could not intend that the law should be enforced against others.[2]

Thus ended the Scopes case, and with it ended—at least for a time—the passage of anti-evolution laws. What the future will bring no one can foretell, but the ridicule heaped upon Tennessee leads one to believe that no state would be likely to follow its example. When an anti-evolution bill was pending recently in the Kentucky legislature, one of the legislators introduced a companion measure reciting that there were other natural phenomena more important to the State of Kentucky than evolution; that every one knows that it is too cold in winter and too warm in summer; and that laws should be passed to compel an even temperature. The bill further referred to the fact that the power situation in Kentucky would be greatly improved if a law were passed that water should run uphill as well as downhill. The Kentucky measure failed.

Those engaged in the Scopes case will ever be grateful to the thousands of people all over the United States who overwhelmed the mail-carriers and the telegraph offices with offers of help and information. One man telegraphed, "Have found missing link. Wire instructions." Another, from San Francisco, "Civilization is at stake. Telephone me at once."

The memory of the Scopes case will undoubtedly live on. The Appellate Court was correct in designating it as a "bizarre" case. Its most intense interest was derived from the clash of the two types of mind. But to-day the statute is generally disregarded in Tennessee. Not

[2] John Thomas Scopes vs. The State of Tennessee, 154 Tenn. 105 (1926).

only this, but interest in the scientific theory of evolution has been greatly increased. Forbidden theories, like forbidden fruit, arouse curiosity, curiosity leads to investigation, investigation to learning. Even though this may result in the specter of skepticism, and in the weakening of faith, the process of mental development cannot be reversed. The stifling of freedom of thought or education often has this effect. Repression always feeds the enemy. . . .

Walter Lippmann : FOUR DIALOGUES

I

DIALOGUE ON OLYMPUS

JEFFERSON, like other enlightened men of his time, believed in the separation of church and state. He wished to disestablish the church, which was then supported out of public funds, and so he declared that taxation for the propagation of opinions in which a man disbelieved was tyranny. But while he said "opinions," he really meant theological opinions. For ardently as he desired to disestablish the church, he no less ardently desired to establish a system of public education. He thought it quite proper to tax the people to support the public schools. For he believed that "by advancing the minds of our youth with the growing science of the times" the public schools would be elevating them "to the practice of the social duties and functions of self-government."

One hundred and forty years later the political leader who in his generation professed to be Jefferson's most loyal disciple, asked whether, if it is wrong to compel people to support a creed they disbelieved, it is not also wrong to compel them to support teaching which impugns the creed in which they do believe. Jefferson had insisted that the people should not have to pay for the teaching of Anglicanism. Mr. Bryan asked why they should be made to pay for the teaching of agnosticism.

Dialogue on Olympus

This was, I believe, a momentous question which we have been too busy to debate. But perhaps by this time, Mr. Jefferson and Mr. Bryan have met on Olympus where there is plenty of time. If they have, let us hope that Socrates is present.

SOCRATES: I have been reading your tombstone, Mr. Jefferson, and I see that you are the author of the Declaration of Independence, the Statute for Religious Freedom, and that you are the Father of the University of Virginia. You do not mention more worldly honors. It is evident that your passion was for liberty and for learning.

JEFFERSON: It was. I had, as I once said to Dr. Rush, sworn upon the altar of God eternal hostility against every form of tyranny over the mind of man.

SOCRATES: And this I believe is Mr. Bryan, three times the chosen leader of the party which you founded.

Reprinted by permission from Walter Lippmann, *American Inquisitors, A Commentary on Dayton and Chicago*, New York, 1928, pp. 13–21, 37–66, 96–110.

JEFFERSON: In a manner of speaking, yes.

SOCRATES: A disciple of yours?

JEFFERSON: You, too, had disciples, I believe.

SOCRATES: Yes, more than I care to remember. They often quarrelled. I shall not go further into that.

JEFFERSON: You were always kind.

SOCRATES: We shall see. I shall ask you a few questions.

BRYAN: Mr. Jefferson can answer them all.

JEFFERSON: I'm not so sure.

BRYAN: A good conscience can answer any question.

SOCRATES: I'm afraid then that I never had a good conscience.

BRYAN: It was good considering that you were a foreigner and a heathen.

SOCRATES: You, too, were accused of being a heathen. Were you not, Mr. Jefferson, accused of being an enemy of religion?

BRYAN (interrupting): That is a foolish question. You may not know it, Mr. Socrates, but he was twice President of the United States.

JEFFERSON: I was denounced as an atheist by many good people.

SOCRATES: Were you an atheist?

JEFFERSON: No, but I disestablished the church in Virginia.

SOCRATES: On what theory?

JEFFERSON: I reflected that the earth was inhabited by a thousand million of people, that these professed probably a thousand different systems of religion; that ours was but one of that thousand; that if there were but one right, and ours that one, we should wish to see the nine hundred and ninety-nine sects gathered into the fold of truth. But against such a majority we could not effect this by force. I said to myself that reason and persuasion are the only practicable in-

struments. To make way for these, free inquiry must be indulged; and how could we wish others to indulge it while we refused it ourselves?

SOCRATES: Had not every state in your day established some religion?

JEFFERSON: That is true. I replied, with some exaggeration I admit, that no two had established the same religion. Was this, I asked, a proof of the infallibility of establishment?

SOCRATES: So you disestablished the church.

BRYAN: He did, sir, and thus proved his sterling Americanism.

SOCRATES: You also, Mr. Bryan, believe in the complete separation of church and state?

BRYAN: I do, sir, most certainly. It is fundamental.

SOCRATES: Can it be done? . . . You look surprised. I was merely wondering.

BRYAN: It has been done in America.

SOCRATES: I won't argue with you about that. I should like to ask Mr. Jefferson some more questions. For example: the church which you disestablished had a creed as to how the world originated, how it is governed, and what men must do to be saved? Had it not?

JEFFERSON: It had.

SOCRATES: And according to the church this creed was a revelation from God. In refusing to pay taxes in support of the teaching of this creed, you asserted, I suppose, that this creed was not revealed by God?

JEFFERSON: Not exactly. I argued that the validity of this creed was a matter for each individual to determine in accordance with his own conscience.

SOCRATES: But all these individuals acting as citizens of the state were to assume, I take it, that God had not revealed the nature of the universe to man.

JEFFERSON: They were free as private

individuals to believe what they liked to believe about that.

SOCRATES: But as citizens they could not believe what they liked?

JEFFERSON: They could not make their private beliefs the official beliefs of the state.

SOCRATES: What then were the official beliefs of the state?

JEFFERSON: There were none. We believed in free inquiry and letting reason prevail.

SOCRATES: I don't understand you. You say there were many people in your day who believed that God had revealed the truth about the universe. You then tell me that officially your citizens had to believe that human reason and not divine revelation was the source of truth and yet you say your state had no official beliefs. It seems to me it had a very definite belief, a belief which contradicts utterly the belief of my friend St. Augustine, for example. Let us be frank. Did you not overthrow a state religion based on revelation and establish in its place the religion of rationalism?

BRYAN: It's getting very warm in here. All this talk makes me very uncomfortable. I don't know what it is leading to.

SOCRATES: I don't either. If I did, I should not be asking questions. What is your answer, Mr. Jefferson?

JEFFERSON: I'll begin by pointing out to you that there was no coercion of opinion. We had no inquisition.

SOCRATES: I understand. But you established public schools and a university?

JEFFERSON: Yes.

SOCRATES: And taxed the people to support them?

JEFFERSON: Yes.

SOCRATES: What was taught in these schools?

JEFFERSON: The best knowledge of the time.

SOCRATES: The knowledge revealed by God?

JEFFERSON: No, the best knowledge acquired by the free use of the human reason.

SOCRATES: And did your taxpayers believe that the best knowledge could be acquired by the human reason?

JEFFERSON: Some believed it. Some preferred revelation.

SOCRATES: And which prevailed?

JEFFERSON: Those who believed in the human reason.

SOCRATES: Were they the majority of the citizens?

JEFFERSON: They must have been. The legislature accepted my plans.

SOCRATES: You believe, Mr. Jefferson, that the majority should rule?

JEFFERSON: Yes, providing it does not infringe the natural rights of man.

SOCRATES: And among the natural rights of man, if I am not mistaken, is, as you once wrote, the right not to be compelled to furnish contributions of money for the propagation of opinions which he disbelieves, and abhors. Mr. Bryan, I think, disbelieves and abhors the opinion that man evolved from a lower form of life.

BRYAN: I do. It is a theory which undermines religion and morality.

SOCRATES: And you objected to being taxed for the teaching of such an opinion?

BRYAN: I most certainly did.

SOCRATES: And you persuaded the representatives of a majority of the voters in one state to forbid this teaching in the schools they were compelled to support.

BRYAN: It was an outrageous misuse of public funds.

SOCRATES: May I ask whether you meant that nobody should be taxed to support the teaching of an opinion which he disbelieves, or whether you meant that the majority shall decide what opinions shall be taught?

BRYAN: I argued that if a majority of the voters in Tennessee believed that Genesis was the true account of creation, they had every right, since they pay for the schools, not to have the minds of their children poisoned.

SOCRATES: But the minority in Tennessee, the modernists, the agnostics, and the unbelievers, also have to pay taxes. Do they not?

BRYAN: The majority must decide.

SOCRATES: Did you say you believe in the separation of church and state?

BRYAN: I did. It is a fundamental principle.

SOCRATES: Is the right of the majority to rule a fundamental principle?

BRYAN: It is.

SOCRATES: Is freedom of thought a fundamental principle, Mr. Jefferson?

JEFFERSON: It is.

SOCRATES: Well, how would you gentlemen compose your fundamental principles, if a majority, exercising its fundamental right to rule, ordained that only Buddhism should be taught in the public schools?

BRYAN: I'd move to a Christian country.

JEFFERSON: I'd exercise the sacred right of revolution. What would you do, Socrates?

SOCRATES: I'd re-examine my fundamental principles.

II

RESUMING ON OLYMPUS: CONCERNING FREEDOM

It is not easy to work out a clear principle which will define the status and function of public school teachers. If you will recall the Dialogue on Olym-

pus in last night's lecture, you will have concluded, I think, that the fundamental principles which we assume to be true are capable of being manipulated to the most surprising and contradictory results. It is possible, for example, to derive the Tennessee statute against evolution from one of the principles laid down in Jefferson's Bill for Establishing Religious Freedom. It is possible to derive justification for an established church from the very arguments used to disestablish a particular church.

Now at the heart of all this confusion we can, I think, distinguish two dogmas. Both of these dogmas are intricate and uncertain. The relation between them is even more intricate and uncertain. I refer to the Dogma of Freedom of Thought and to the Dogma of Popular Rule.

Resuming on Olympus: Concerning Freedom

For the analysis of the implications of an idea we have no more convenient instrument than the Socratic dialogue. So with your permission I shall resume the Dialogue on Olympus at the point where it was broken off, last night.

JEFFERSON: You were saying, Socrates, that it would be well to examine these conflicting fundamental principles. I offer you as a beginning the principle laid down in my Notes on Viriginia that reason and free inquiry are the only effectual agents against error.

SOCRATES: I believe that was not a new principle in your day?

JEFFERSON: Indeed it was not. You practiced it yourself.

SOCRATES: So I did. There were others before me. I remember Protagoras who wrote a book *On the Gods*,—our gods, Mr. Bryan—which began: "Concerning the gods, I cannot say that they exist nor yet that they do not exist. There are more reasons than one why we cannot know. There is the obscurity of the subject and there is the brevity of human life." His books were collected and burned. Reason has never been popular.

JEFFERSON: It will prevail.

SOCRATES: What will prevail?

JEFFERSON: Reason will prevail. Galileo was sent to the Inquisition in 1616. But his book was taken off the Roman Index in 1835.

SOCRATES: So in this case it took only 219 years for reason to prevail. Why did it take so long?

BRYAN: The vested interests of the church were too strong for the people.

SOCRATES: I was put to death by vote of the people. The authorities would have been glad to have me escape. It was the triumph of democracy which finished me.

BRYAN: The people are sometimes misled.

SOCRATES: I dare say. The persecution of the Christians was rather provoked by the populace than desired by the authorities. The Inquisition was very popular in its day. When the Pope and the Bishops relented, public opinion insisted upon the extermination of the heretics. The people are still like that down there below. It was, I think, the Great Commoner who led the last crusade against science. It is the newspapers of the larger circulations, which appeal to the great mass of the people, who are always smelling out treason in the schools.

JEFFERSON: And what do you conclude from all this?

SOCRATES: That the common people hate reason, and that reason is the religion of an elite, of great gentlemen like yourself.

BRYAN: Reason a religion? What do you mean?

SOCRATES: The common people have always known that reason is a religion. That is why they dislike it so violently.

JEFFERSON: Please speak more plainly.

SOCRATES: You advocated the use of reason and free inquiry. What for?

JEFFERSON: I said: "Give a loose to them, they will support the true religion by bringing every false one to their tribunal, to the test of their investigation."

SOCRATES: You said "their tribunal," the tribunal of reason and free inquiry. I suppose these false religions, as you call them, also had a tribunal to which they summoned beliefs. What was that tribunal?

JEFFERSON: It was usually called revelation.

SOCRATES: And it was your theory that religions based on divine revelation should be investigated before the tribunal of human reason?

JEFFERSON: Yes.

SOCRATES: That God's Word should be tested by human words? What makes you so confident about human reason?

JEFFERSON: Many statements purporting to be revealed truth are demonstrably false. They can easily be disproved.

SOCRATES: Have not many statements based on reason turned out to be demonstrably false?

JEFFERSON: Their error has been exposed by reason and corrected by reason.

SOCRATES: So the difference between revelation and reason is that conclusions based on revelation cannot be corrected, but that conclusions based on reason can always be corrected.

JEFFERSON: That is right.

SOCRATES: Then you can never be sure that a conclusion reached by reason is finally correct?

BRYAN: I demonstrated that at Day-

ton. I quoted several biologists who dis-
agreed with Darwin.

SOCRATES: Did these biologists of yours
say they had at last got the whole truth?

BRYAN: I don't think they did.

SOCRATES: So in this realm of reason
you are never very sure of anything.

JEFFERSON: You must always keep your
mind open for new evidence.

SOCRATES: Then if I understand you
correctly a reasonable man is one who
does not believe very firmly in his own
reason.

JEFFERSON: He trusts his reason but
he distrusts his conclusions.

BRYAN: This is getting very complicated.

SOCRATES: Well, it is complicated. Mr.
Jefferson says that a man must believe
that reason will give him the truth, but
he must not believe too strongly that he
has the truth when he has reasoned it
out.

JEFFERSON: The work of reason is never finished.

SOCRATES: You wish men to believe in
reason, but not in their reasoning at any
particular moment. Is that it?

JEFFERSON: That is what is now called
the scientific spirit.

SOCRATES: Does one not need faith to
believe that reason, though never wholly
successful, will at last conquer reality?

JEFFERSON: Sublime faith.

SOCRATES: Perhaps more faith than the
ordinary man can feel?

JEFFERSON: What are you leading to?

SOCRATES: To an explanation of why
the people reject reason though it has
been consciously practised for two thousand years.

JEFFERSON: In the end they accept it.
But it is a long and often a bitter struggle.

SOCRATES: Do they accept reason, or

do they accept some conclusion at which
reason has happened to arrive?

JEFFERSON: The scientific method is
widely practised now.

SOCRATES: I grant you that. Reason has
more devotees than it ever had before.
But they are still a minority. I return to
my question: is it a victory for reason if
the people at last accept what they once
regarded as dangerous heresy?

JEFFERSON: Not necessarily.

SOCRATES: Why not necessarily?

JEFFERSON: Because, as you so cun-
ningly pointed out, the conclusions
reached by reason are not final. By the
time the people accept a rational conclusion, it may no longer be rational.
You would say, I suppose, that in twenty-
five years the mountaineers of Tennessee
will swear by Darwin as violently as
they now swear at him.

BRYAN: I can say in this connection
that having had an opportunity to meet
Mr. Darwin, it is evident that he is a
kindly, patient, and forbearing man.

SOCRATES: Yes, he will make an excellent saint in the church which Clarence
Darrow is founding.

BRYAN: I didn't know that Mr. Darrow was a churchman.

SOCRATES: Neither does Mr. Darrow.
But he is. When Mr. Darrow was younger than he is today, scientific men found
the hypothesis of mechanism rather convenient. Mr. Darrow has been teaching
this hypothesis as gospel ever since. He
is very orthodox. It is a sad and kindly
religion which may have quite a vogue.

JEFFERSON: Does it persecute unbelievers?

SOCRATES: No. Mr. Darrow merely
makes them look foolish. But that hurts.

BRYAN: It does.

JEFFERSON: It would be better, as I
told Livingston at the end of my life
on earth, if men learned to be less con-

fident in the conclusions of human reason and to give more credit to the honesty of contrary opinions.

SOCRATES: You may remember that in the Laws of Manu it is enjoined on the Brahman that when his hair is white, and his skin is wrinkled, and he has looked on his son's sons, he shall turn his back on his home and his ordinary affairs, and withdrawing to the forest, shall devote the remainder of his days to meditation on the nature of the Infinite Being. When you wrote that to Livingston you had become the Sage of Monticello. You had turned your back on men.

JEFFERSON: I was consulted by all kinds of men to the end of my days.

SOCRATES: But you had forgotten what men are like if you thought they could endure it not to be confident of their conclusions.

JEFFERSON: Explain yourself.

SOCRATES: I feel that I am going to make a speech.

BRYAN: I shall like it.

JEFFERSON: I don't think I shall. I once told the president of a debating society that most oratory is an insult to an assembly of reasonable men, disgusting and revolting, instead of persuading. Speeches measured by the hour die with the hour.

SOCRATES: You rather enjoy quoting yourself.

JEFFERSON: No, these speeches are being put into my mouth.

SOCRATES: So are mine being put into my mouth.

BRYAN: Newspapermen like to put words into people's mouths.

SOCRATES: I do not complain. I am going to deliver my speech.

JEFFERSON: What were we talking about?

SOCRATES: I was about to explain why men cannot endure not being confident of their conclusions. And I was going to say that most men have no time for speculation. They have too many immediate worries. Ideas are of no use to them unless they provide means of dealing with the things that worry them. They feel insecure. They have to make a living, and they are constantly menaced by this and that, by drought and plagues, by wars and oppressions, by disease and death. An easy and tolerant skepticism is not for them. They want ideas which they can count upon, sure cures, absolute promises, and no shilly-shallying with a lot of ifs and perhaps. The faith of the people is always hard, practical, and definite. And that is why your religion of reason is not for them.

JEFFERSON: Because it denies them hard and fast conclusions on which they can rely absolutely?

SOCRATES: Yes. Have you ever stopped to think what it means when a man acquires the scientific spirit? It means that he is ready to let things be what they may be, whether or not he wants them to be that way. It means that he has conquered his desire to have the world justify his prejudices. It means that he has learned how to live without the support of any creed, that he can be happy, or at least serene, that he can be good, or at least humane, no matter what conclusion men may come to as to the origin of the world, or its plan, or its destiny. There are not many men of this sort in any age.

JEFFERSON: Utterly self-sufficient and disinterested men. Are they the only ones who can endure complete freedom of thought?

SOCRATES: They are the only ones. If a man has wants he must pay the price. If he wants gold and silver and big estates, he must want the kind of society in which it is possible for him to have these things. If he wants a heaven of material well-being, he must want the kind of universe which will guarantee him such a heaven. It is only when he has ceased to care about the result that he can trust himself wholly to free inquiry.

JEFFERSON: Must a man then surrender everything if he is to be free?

SOCRATES: That was my conclusion. That is why I refused to flee to Thessaly when they left the prison door open for me. Had I run away in order to be able to eat a few more dinners, I should have been not a philosopher but the slave of my own stomach. Had I submitted to that, could I ever again have been sure that what I thought was the voice of reason was not in fact the rumbling of my own stomach?

JEFFERSON: Is freedom as difficult as you make it out?

SOCRATES: Not quite. I am now a legend devised by Plato to instruct mankind.

JEFFERSON: You mean that freedom may not require the complete renunciation of worldly desires?

SOCRATES: I mean that freedom may also be a matter of degree, and that men could enjoy a good deal of freedom if, while following their worldly desires, they did not think very highly of any of them.

JEFFERSON: But you said that most men were too preoccupied with the problem of living to look at life in this fashion.

SOCRATES: I adhere to that. And while mankind is thus preoccupied it will neither enjoy freedom itself nor tolerate too much of it in others. I was thinking of a considerable minority which now exists for the first time in the history of mankind, a class who no longer really need to worry about their safety or whether they can earn enough to live.

JEFFERSON: They may have other worries. Have you noticed the divorce courts down there?

SOCRATES: I am not a reformer. I was merely going to say that when the necessities of life are secure, a man can begin to be free. We in Athens founded our freedom on chattel slavery. So I think did you. You have got to found it on something. If they can do it with machines and organization and wise laws, well and good. The point is that a man can only begin to be disinterested when he has ceased to be hungry and uncomfortable and frightened. I was free because I wanted so little. You were free because you wanted nothing more. But people are never free who want more than they can have. Their wants create worries, their worries create prejudices, their prejudices demand guaranties, and under freedom of thought nothing is guaranteed.

III

DIALOGUE AT DAYTON

In the light of this analysis I should like to consider sympathetically the state of mind of a taxpayer in Tennessee who favored the passage of the so-called anti-evolution bill. That state of mind is fairly represented, I imagine, by a letter which appeared in the Knoxville News at the time of the controversy. The writer, after remonstrating with the newspaper for its failure to treat the law respectfully, concludes by saying: "The anti-evolution law prohibits the teaching that the world was created in any way except as set forth in Genesis. That is as it should be. Our children can now go to school without having all their faith and hope destroyed by science." [1]

MODERNIST: I don't see what difference

[1] Quoted in Maynard Shipley, *The War on Modern Science*, p. 220.

it makes to faith and hope whether the world was created as set forth in Genesis or not. I could join you in insisting upon the moral truth of the Sermon on the Mount, but why do you insist upon the scientific truth of Genesis?

FUNDAMENTALIST: If I deny the teaching of Genesis, what assurance have I about the teaching in Luke, Matthew or Mark?

MODERNIST: The teachings of the Gospels are verified by the religious and moral experience of men. That is your assurance. But the teaching of Genesis runs counter to the knowledge of men.

FUNDAMENTALIST: This comes down to saying that I am to pick and choose what parts of the Bible I shall believe.

MODERNIST: Are you not a Protestant? Do you not believe in the right of private judgment?

FUNDAMENTALIST: Had you studied history a little more carefully you would not ask this question. You might examine Luther's views on Zwingli and on the Anabaptists.

MODERNIST: You mean that the right of private judgment was not a principle in Luther's teaching, but a method, provisionally adopted, for dealing with the authority of the Pope?

FUNDAMENTALIST: I do. For me the hope of salvation depends upon the authority of the Scriptures.

MODERNIST: The account of creation in Genesis has nothing to do with the promise of salvation.

FUNDAMENTALIST: You are quite wrong. It would make no difference if the Bible had said that the world was created in seven million years rather than in seven days or that man was descended from an ape. I could believe that as readily as I believe what I now believe. The important question is not what the Bible says about creation, but that the Bible says it. If the Bible is wrong about creation, how am I to know that it is not also wrong about salvation? I say to my children: You must not steal. . . . You must not lie. . . . You must keep the Ten Commandments. . . . You must follow the teachings of the Sermon on the Mount. . . . They say to me: Why should we do that? . . . I tell them it is God's will. They say to me: How do you know it is God's will? I reply: Because Scripture is the word of God divinely inspired. And then they say: Yes, but teacher says the Bible is wrong when it tells that woman was made from Adam's rib.

MODERNIST: Must your children then believe what is untrue in order that they may believe what is true?

FUNDAMENTALIST: I don't know that Genesis is untrue. Neither do you. You weren't there at the creation and neither was Darwin. Your scientists are all at sixes and sevens, and none of them even pretends to know how the world came to be created.

MODERNIST: They know it could not have been created as set forth in Genesis.

FUNDAMENTALIST: They do, do they? Well, what if they do?

MODERNIST: Don't you want your children to respect the truth?

FUNDAMENTALIST: Indeed I do. That is just where I quarrel with modernism. It undermines the respect of my children for the truth. They learn a lot of half-baked theories about evolution in school, and then they come home disbelieving the whole religion and morality of their fathers, and recognizing no standards of conduct except their own wilfulness.

MODERNIST: You are going to ask me to believe that the whole of religion and morality rests upon an old Jewish legend about the creation?

FUNDAMENTALIST: I am going to ask you to tell me what guarantee there is

for religion and morality if you ~~first re-~~
~~ject the authority of the Catholic Church,~~
~~as Protestants do, and then proceed to~~
reject the authority of the Bible, as you
~~modernists~~ do?

MODERNIST: We do not reject the authority of the Bible. We hold that it is
profoundly inspired.

FUNDAMENTALIST: Is the whole Bible
inspired?

MODERNIST: Not all of it. The Bible is
a vast literature not all written at one
time and by no means all of the same
quality. The Bible is not a single book.

FUNDAMENTALIST: Then how do you
know which parts of the Bible are, ~~as~~
~~you say, profoundly~~ inspired?

MODERNIST: Those parts are inspired
which are verified by the religious experience of mankind.

FUNDAMENTALIST: And how do you
know that the religious experience of
mankind is reliable? Do all modernists
agree on what they will regard as the
profoundly inspired parts of the Bible?

MODERNIST: There is some disagree-
ment.

FUNDAMENTALIST: So that one modernist ~~might~~ call one part of the Bible inspired and another modernist ~~might~~ not.

MODERNIST: That is so.

FUNDAMENTALIST: Then perhaps you
will tell me how I am to convince my
children that any part of the Bible is
inspired.

MODERNIST: You must enlarge their experience and train their judgment. Then
they can decide for themselves.

FUNDAMENTALIST: They are to decide
for themselves what is moral and immoral?

MODERNIST: They must learn to be
guided in their decisions by the accumulated wisdom of the race.

FUNDAMENTALIST: Guided by it. But
not bound by it?

MODERNIST: It is impossible to lay
down absolute rules which will be valid
in all cases.

FUNDAMENTALIST: So we have come to
the conclusion that it is impossible to
know for certain what God's will is. It
is equally impossible to know for certain
what the so-called wisdom of mankind is.
Each youngster, therefore, is, under your
system, to face the temptations and the
perplexities of the world with nothing
more than a tentative moral code which
he is at liberty to revise as he sees fit.
How do you distinguish this beautiful
theory from sheer moral anarchy?

MODERNIST: You have got to have some
faith in the common sense and decent
instincts of your fellow men.

FUNDAMENTALIST: Have you such
faith?

MODERNIST: Yes. Haven't you?

FUNDAMENTALIST: No. I haven't. Such
a faith is contradicted by that experience
of mankind to which you are so fond of
appealing. Your natural man is a natural
barbarian, grasping, selfish, lustful, mur-
derous. Your psychoanalysts will tell you
that. The religious teachers knew it long
before the psychoanalysts rediscovered
it. They called it original sin. They knew
man was unworthy until he had been redeemed, or as you would say, educated.

MODERNIST: And what does that prove?

FUNDAMENTALIST: That even if the
modernists could agree upon a moral
code, they could not inculcate morality.
For the moral life is due not to the acceptance of a set of rules but to a transformation of the will.

MODERNIST: And what have you to offer that will transform the will except the
kindly advice and the good example of
the wise?

FUNDAMENTALIST: I have the knowledge that I am part of a universe governed by a divine plan to which, if I wish

to be everlastingly happy, I must make my will conform.

MODERNIST: In order to be good is it necessary to believe all that? Have there not been good men who disbelieved it?

FUNDAMENTALIST: No doubt there have been. Yet you will not deny that the great mass of mankind has always insisted upon believing that it was in communion with, and subject to, a will greater than its own. Do you know of any popular morality in the history of the world which has not had some sort of supernatural sanction?

MODERNIST: I do not know of any popular morality. But I know that there have been men who lived nobly without supernatural sanction.

FUNDAMENTALIST: Is it your hope, then, that what a few men have done all men might ultimately do?

MODERNIST: That is, I suppose, the faith of the modernist.

FUNDAMENTALIST: Are you not rather an optimist?

MODERNIST: In what respect?

FUNDAMENTALIST: You admit that all history shows how few men have been able to live a moral life without the conviction that they were obeying a divine will. You then point out a few unusual men, a few stoics perhaps, a few Epicureans, a few followers of Spinoza, a few pure and disinterested spirits among the scientists, and you ask me to believe that what this trifling minority has achieved through innate moral genius, the great humdrum mass of mankind is to achieve by what you optimistically describe as education. I do not believe it.

MODERNIST: If I accepted your argument I should be forced to the conclusion that the mass of mankind are incapable of receiving the truth.

FUNDAMENTALIST: That horrifies you?

MODERNIST: It does indeed.

FUNDAMENTALIST: I thought you had solemnly sworn to follow the truth wherever it might lead. But when you are confronted with the possibility that mankind cannot receive truth, you shrink from that truth. Does that not rather tend to confirm my suggestion that the appetite for truth is not so strong after all?

MODERNIST: That is an ingenious paradox and I haven't time to unravel it. Come back to the main point. You were saying that only a small minority has ever found the moral life possible without the absolute assurance that it was obeying a divine will.

FUNDAMENTALIST: And you were admitting that the task of modernism is to teach the vast majority to live as only this small minority has previously lived. I was expressing my doubts as to whether the modernists would succeed.

MODERNIST: Are they not compelled to try?

FUNDAMENTALIST: I'll let you answer that.

MODERNIST: Then I should say that nothing can now arrest the penetration of the scientific spirit into every field of opinion. You do not seriously think your laws against Darwin and the rest are effective?

FUNDAMENTALIST: Apparently they are not.

MODERNIST: Then what you call unbelief—that is, disbelief that there exists an authoritative account of destiny—is bound to infect the whole population. That being the fact, is it not our task to prepare men to lead independent, rational lives?

FUNDAMENTALIST: I might grant you that unbelief is bound for the time to spread. But I cannot believe you will succeed in teaching the great mass of men to lead independent, rational lives.

MODERNIST: You believe that all men are the children of God?

FUNDAMENTALIST: I do. And that most of them are children.

MODERNIST: That they are endowed by their Creator with reason and conscience?

FUNDAMENTALIST: Yes.

MODERNIST: Why then deny to the humblest that salvation which some of the greatest have found?

FUNDAMENTALIST: You are argumentative, and you are very naive.

MODERNIST: If there is one thing we modernists are not, it is naive. We are highly sophisticated people.

FUNDAMENTALIST: I withdraw the word *naive*. You are merely ignorant. You have never studied the history of religions. Naturally you are ignorant.

MODERNIST: I have studied the history of religions.

FUNDAMENTALIST: Then how could you have failed to observe that the greatest teachers, Jesus, St. Paul, Buddha, Plato, Spinoza, all of them, taught that the perfect life was too difficult for the mass of men, that it required discipline and renunciation which most men could not endure, that it was in fact beyond their moral capacities?

MODERNIST: You mean that "narrow is the gate"?

FUNDAMENTALIST: I do. Spinoza said that the way of salvation must be hard or it would not be by almost all men neglected.

MODERNIST: What you are saying now seems to destroy what you were saying before. You began by asking me how you could convince your children that they should accept morality if they were not first convinced that it is God's will. Now you are saying that it is extremely difficult for most men to obey God's will.

FUNDAMENTALIST: The great religious teachers, my friend, reached up to heaven, but their feet were firmly planted upon the earth. They had no illusions, as you have, about the capacities of men. That is why every important religion contains every grade of teaching from the grossest superstition to the purest expression of the spirit. Nobody who examines Buddhism or Christianity can have the slightest doubt that they have been adapted in the course of time to all the different intellectual and moral levels of mankind.

MODERNIST: And what do you deduce from these rather broad and doubtful generalizations of yours?

FUNDAMENTALIST: I deduce the extremely important conclusion that modernists are trying to grow grapes from thistles. And that that is a rather naive thing to do.

MODERNIST: I told you once that I objected to the word *naive*.

FUNDAMENTALIST: Well, I don't know what to call it. But are you not in fact blithely proposing to teach the scientific method to a mass of people who haven't the remotest chance of understanding it?

MODERNIST: I said we were compelled to try because the supernatural systems of authority were ceasing to be credible in the modern world.

FUNDAMENTALIST: That you are helping to break down the supernatural systems of authority I won't deny. But that you are teaching men to do without them I am not so sure.

MODERNIST: Why should you be so doubtful? The western world was once pagan. Then it became Catholic. Then a part of it became Protestant. Why should it not now become scientific?

FUNDAMENTALIST: Because this last

change calls for the profoundest change in the habits of the human mind which has ever taken place. It means that men must learn to act with certainty upon premises which are uncertain. Your scientific method cannot guarantee its conclusions beyond all shadow of doubt.

MODERNIST: Of course it cannot.

FUNDAMENTALIST: But the mass of men won't tolerate this much uncertainty. They are not sufficiently disinterested. They will make incontrovertible dogmas out of scientific hypotheses. You are not teaching science when you teach a child that the earth moves around the sun rather than, as the Bible teaches, that the sun moves around the earth.

MODERNIST: I know that.

FUNDAMENTALIST: So that what your scientific education comes down to is this. A minority, perhaps a slowly growing minority, acquire the scientific habit of mind and learn to live the disinterested kind of life which science demands. But the rest merely acquire odds and ends of more or less obsolete information which, while it destroys the authority and the majesty of their inherited religion, is in itself morally worthless. It fits into no plan, it supports no ideal of life. It provides no background for the human spirit.

MODERNIST: I find all this rather depressing.

FUNDAMENTALIST: I remind you again that as a modernist you are a devotee of the truth.

MODERNIST: What truth are you talking about?

FUNDAMENTALIST: A truth which shatters many pretences and illuminates some of the confusion of the modern mind.

MODERNIST: I am all agog to hear this truth.

FUNDAMENTALIST: Then you shall hear it. In our public controversies you are fond of arguing that you are open-minded, tolerant and neutral in the face of conflicting opinions. That is not so. You are fond of arguing that the conclusions of science can be reconciled with the conclusions of theology. That is evasive. These claims deceive nobody. They are merely adopted as convenient pretences by the politically minded, the timid, and the superficial. You know and I know that the issue is not whether Adam was created at nine o'clock in the morning or whether he descended from an ape. The issue is whether there exists a Book which, because it is divinely inspired, can be regarded by men as the "infallible rule of faith and practice," or whether men must rely upon human reason alone, and henceforth do without an infallible rule of faith and practice. What you challenge is not Genesis but revelation, and what I am defending ultimately is the faith of men that they know the Word of God.

I would ask you therefore not to be confused by the incidental ignorance of your partisans and of mine. It is of no consequence in itself whether the earth is flat or round. But it is of transcendent importance whether man can commune with God and obey His directions, or whether he must trust his own conscience and reason to find his way through the jungle of life. On that question it is impossible for an honest man to be neutral. It is impossible for him to be tolerant. It is impossible for him to be open-minded.

MODERNIST: I don't see that.

FUNDAMENTALIST: You can say: Maybe Darwin is right . . . maybe Lamarck is right . . . perhaps Einstein is right . . . perhaps he isn't . . . That is your scientific spirit. But you can't say: Perhaps the word of God is right and perhaps it isn't.

MODERNIST: Why can't you?

FUNDAMENTALIST: Because the authority of the Bible rests upon revelation, and if you are open-minded about revelation you simply do not believe in it. Doubt is an essential part of the method of science, but it is the negation of faith. To say that you are open-minded about the inspiration of the Bible is nonsense. Open-mindedness in this connection is a perfectly definite rejection of the Bible's inspiration.

MODERNIST: I don't understand.

FUNDAMENTALIST: What do you mean by open-mindedness?

MODERNIST: A refusal to reach a conclusion on the ground that the evidence is not conclusive.

FUNDAMENTALIST: Exactly. But those who believe in the divine authority of the Bible believe it on grounds which are beyond the reach of human inquiry and evidence. Once you subject that authority to the test of human reason you have denied the essence of its authority. You have made the finite understanding the judge of the infinite. You are then, in the historic meaning of the word, an unbeliever.

MODERNIST: Is there no way out of this conflict?

FUNDAMENTALIST: That is not for me to say. I speak for the ancient and established order of mankind. You are the newcomer. You are the rebel. I do not know what you are going to do about it. You can disguise this issue but you cannot obliterate it.

MODERNIST: We can at least discuss it like gentlemen, without heat, without rancor.

FUNDAMENTALIST: Has it ever occurred to you that this advice is easier for you to follow than for me?

MODERNIST: How so?

FUNDAMENTALIST: Because for me an eternal plan of salvation is at stake. For you there is nothing at stake but a few tentative opinions none of which means anything to your happiness. Your request that I should be tolerant and amiable is, therefore, a suggestion that I submit the foundation of my life to the destructive effects of your skepticism, your indifference, and your good nature. You ask me to smile and to commit suicide. . . .

IV

DIALOGUE IN AMERICA: CONCERNING MAJORITY RULE

I shall suppose that the teacher finds himself in a community like Dayton or Chicago, where an effective majority of the voters is insisting that he shall make the schools safe for some kind of fundamentalism.

SOCRATES: The question you are asking yourself is what respect you ought to have in your own mind for the wishes of a majority. What then do you mean by wishes?

TEACHER: I mean the wish that in teaching science I shall not impugn revelation and that in teaching history I shall not impugn tradition.

SOCRATES: You being yourself one who accepts the authority of reason?

TEACHER: Yes.

SOCRATES: Then you cannot accept the authority of revelation or of tradition?

TEACHER: No. But I am employed by people a majority of whom do accept it.

SOCRATES: Have you complete confidence in reason?

TEACHER: In reason, yes.—In my reasoning, no.

SOCRATES: You feel that you may be

wrong, and that the majority may be right.

TEACHER: Surely that is possible.

SOCRATES: Do you feel that the opinions of the majority may be right because they are the opinions of the majority?

TEACHER: Sometimes. But not always. The difficulty is to know when. There is some kind of wisdom in numbers.

SOCRATES: Your task then is to find out, if you can, what kind of wisdom there is in numbers.

TEACHER: Yes. It is plain, I think, that the majority is often wrong. It is equally plain that the educated minority has often been wrong.

SOCRATES: Then perhaps being right or wrong has nothing to do with majorities and minorities.

TEACHER: I am not satisfied with that. There are times, I believe, when an opinion is entitled to particular respect because it is the opinion of the majority.

SOCRATES: It would have to be the kind of opinion about which the majority was competent to have an opinion. Would it not?

TEACHER: Obviously.

SOCRATES: Is the majority competent to have an opinion about physics and biology?

TEACHER: I am sure it is not. You cannot settle scientific controversies by the election returns.

SOCRATES: But you settle great human problems by the election returns. And these problems are more important in your lives than any problem in physics or biology.

TEACHER: We do not settle great human problems by the election returns. We find out which party is the stronger. We decide between two or more courses of action.

SOCRATES: Then what you can learn from the majority is what the majority intends to do or consents to have done.

TEACHER: That is about what political democracy amounts to. Power today resides in numbers. It is necessary, therefore, for governments to satisfy numbers.

SOCRATES: Regardless of whether the majority is right or wrong?

TEACHER: In government it is necessary to know what the majority wants and what it will tolerate before you can know what is right or wrong. To act without that is to invite revolution.

SOCRATES: Then what the majority knows is what the majority wants. The people are experts on the subject of their own desires.

TEACHER: Not so very expert at that. They often do not know what they want. Less often do they know what they will want.

SOCRATES: Is it not so that they at least know at any particular moment what they think they want?

TEACHER: That much not even Mr. Mencken would deny.

SOCRATES: Pardon me, did I hear you say "Mr. Mencken"? I haven't met him.

TEACHER: A charming fellow, I assure you. You'll meet him soon.

SOCRATES: Then he is still alive,—but failing?

TEACHER: Yes. He can't last long, poor fellow. He is about to laugh himself to death. He has uncontrollable fits of merriment over his discovery that mankind is foolish.

SOCRATES: *His* discovery?

TEACHER: Well, he acts as if it were his discovery.

SOCRATES: It isn't.

TEACHER: I'm sorry I mentioned him. You never lived in America, so you cannot appreciate what a good man he is.

SOCRATES: Well, you did not have to mention him, did you?

TEACHER: I couldn't help it. I thought of him when you said the people know at any particular moment what they think they want.

SOCRATES: Does he admit that?

TEACHER: If he ever admitted anything, I think he would admit that.

SOCRATES: Do you think he would admit that the people know anything besides what they think they want?

TEACHER: God forbid that a poor pedagogue should speak for H. L. Mencken.

SOCRATES: He must be an awe-inspiring fellow. Well, what is the poor pedagogue prepared to admit here where H. L. Mencken can't bawl him out?

TEACHER: That the judgment of many men might at times be wiser than the judgment of a few men.

SOCRATES: Certainly. But what judgments?

TEACHER: Those in which racial instincts ought to play a part.

SOCRATES: Can you define that?

TEACHER: No, but I feel in my bones that there are many momentous things about which the sense of ordinary men may be more reliable than the opinions of experts and theorists.

SOCRATES: Can you not feel it in *your* bones when such a question has arisen?

TEACHER: The feelings in my bones are not so trustworthy as they were. They are confused by learning. I am analytical. I am self-conscious. I can no longer trust my bones.

SOCRATES: You have admitted that the opinions of the majority are absolutely reliable as to what the majority thinks it wants. You then go on and suggest that in various vague but important matters the intuitions of the majority may be

wise. But you do not know what those matters are?

TEACHER: I don't.

SOCRATES: They could not be matters upon which science has passed judgment after thorough investigation?

TEACHER: No.

SOCRATES: Then they must be matters upon which science has not passed judgment?

TEACHER: I think so.

SOCRATES: On these you are inclined to trust the judgment of the majority?

TEACHER: I am not wholly certain.

SOCRATES: Is the judgment of the majority upon these great unsettled questions always perfectly clear?

TEACHER: It is rarely perfectly clear. It is often difficult to know what the majority thinks.

SOCRATES: How is that?

TEACHER: Well, the judgment of the majority in one of the five counties of a city like New York may differ from the judgment of a majority in the whole city. This majority may differ from the majority in the whole state. The state's majority may differ from the nation's. The nation's may differ from that of mankind.

SOCRATES: Then when you speak of a majority you really have to say first how many are to be included in the count?

TEACHER: Yes, and there are many ways of arranging the population so as to get the result you want. It is known in politics as gerrymandering.

SOCRATES: Would you ascribe the same mystic wisdom to any majority of any group no matter how it was gerrymandered?

TEACHER: That would make nonsense of the whole idea.

SOCRATES: Then the group in which the opinions of the majority are entitled to special respect must be a particular sort of group?

TEACHER: Yes.

SOCRATES: Particular in what way?

TEACHER: It must not be an artificial political grouping.

SOCRATES: Those are vague words.

TEACHER: This is a subtle idea. I hardly know how to define it.

SOCRATES: Well, remember that you were looking for the occasions when you ought to trust the common sense of ordinary men. Do you not have to say then that they must be occasions in which the common experience of ordinary men is significant?

TEACHER: And then what?

SOCRATES: Must they not be occasions of which all of the ordinary men you consult have had experience?

TEACHER: I think so.

SOCRATES: Then the group whose majority you respect must be a group of men who are closely related to one another in the matter which interests them. A family's opinion about the concerns of that family. A village's opinion about the concerns of that village. A city's opinion about the concerns of that city.

TEACHER: When you get to the city I am not so sure. If you went on to a nation I'd be even less sure.

SOCRATES: Why is that?

TEACHER: Because in a city and in a nation there is little direct common experience. Most of the common experience is vicarious and deals with invisible matters uncertainly reported.

SOCRATES: The factor of error and deception enters?

TEACHER: All manner of illusion and what people now call propaganda.

SOCRATES: What is propaganda?

TEACHER: The art of controlling judgment by provoking false images to awaken prejudices.

SOCRATES: You call it an art.

TEACHER: One of the most potent in the modern world.

SOCRATES: To what do you ascribe its potency?

TEACHER: To the fact that mankind now lives in a society which is so large that no man can see much of it. We are all dependent upon others for our knowledge of this society. We have not yet learned how to make that knowledge trustworthy. This is the propagandist's opportunity.

SOCRATES: The propagandist can, I suppose, assemble majorities.

TEACHER: He can and he does.

SOCRATES: And to such majorities you do not wish to give any respect whatever?

TEACHER: I do not wish to, but I can't always help myself. Often it is not possible, moreover, to know whether the majority speaks a real judgment or repeats what propagandists have told it.

SOCRATES: The majorities which are drawn from large and more or less artificial groups are the least respectable.

TEACHER: They are the most powerful.

SOCRATES: We are not discussing power. We are discussing wisdom.

TEACHER: Then the opinions of the small homogeneous community in respect to its own concerns would be, I should say, the most respectable.

SOCRATES: Aristotle got as far as that.

TEACHER: We have not gotten much further.

SOCRATES: Your conclusion then is that this mystic wisdom of the people is most likely to appear in small groups dealing with their own affairs?

TEACHER: It is not likely to appear when they are dealing with other people's affairs, though most men seem to think so nowadays. And it is not likely to appear in large groups dealing with matters they know only by hearsay and can't very well understand. There can't be much wisdom in that.

SOCRATES: You are not, however, opposed to political democracy?

TEACHER: Am I opposed to the weather? On cold rainy days I am. The fact of democracy is as little subject to discussion in the modern world as the weather. Even dictators have to consult or cajole the people. There are two kinds of muddleheadedness in our own age on this question: there are the muddleheaded people who think the people are wise and the muddleheaded people who think they are foolish. Now Mr. Mencken—

SOCRATES: You were sorry the last time you mentioned him.

TEACHER: I won't mention him though it is a little like trying not to think of a white elephant for ten consecutive minutes.

SOCRATES: You were not talking about Mr. Mencken or about white elephants. You were talking of muddleheaded people.

TEACHER: Yes, and I was about to say that they are muddleheaded because they judge democracy from the point of view of what is wise and of what is unwise, when as a matter of fact political democracy is a matter of finding out who intends to have the last word, and then of having the government behave accordingly.

SOCRATES: Then to the expressions of political democracy you give no inward respect whatever?

TEACHER: Ought I to?

SOCRATES: The majority is sovereign. Ought the sovereign not to be respected?

TEACHER: We have already discussed the difficulties, have we not?

SOCRATES: Yes, but your conclusion is a little puzzling. You have no inward respect for the opinions of most majori-

ties. Can you obey a sovereign whose opinions you do not respect?

TEACHER: Can I serve that sovereign if I do respect his opinions?

SOCRATES: Never mind the paradoxes.

TEACHER: The relation of an individual to democracy is a paradox. If everyone respected the opinions of the majority, those opinions would never improve. If everybody defied the opinions of the majority, there would be no government. And therefore no use in trying to improve the opinions of the majority.

SOCRATES: Your sovereign under democracy is a peculiar person.

TEACHER: He is not a person. He is many persons and not the same ones every day.

SOCRATES: Perhaps that is where your paradoxes arise. This democratic sovereign is not a person. It is a changing array of individuals. You may be part of the sovereign power one day and not the next.

TEACHER: Precisely.

SOCRATES: On the day when you are not part of it, you are one of the Outs hoping to become one of the Ins?

TEACHER: Or at least hoping to teach the Ins some better sense.

SOCRATES: Then whether you are out or in you are always helping to create the sovereign in a democracy?

TEACHER: In a manner of speaking.

SOCRATES: When you join the crowd you add to its force. When you resist the crowd, what happens to you?

TEACHER: I may lose my job. I may be pushed aside. I may be trampled upon.

SOCRATES: Is that the only fate of those who resist the crowd?

TEACHER: A very few become the leaders of the crowd.

SOCRATES: Is that all?

TEACHER: A few are cranks and fools.

SOCRATES: Is that all?

TEACHER: A few are martyrs and geniuses.

SOCRATES: What about those who go with the crowd. Are they all fools?

TEACHER: Certainly not.

SOCRATES: Are they all wise men?

TEACHER: Obviously not.

SOCRATES: Then to go with the crowd or against it is in itself no sign of wisdom or folly?

TEACHER: But we started out to see whether a man should respect or defy the crowd.

SOCRATES: And we have concluded that the majority is entitled to no particular respect. And that it is entitled to no particular disrespect. And that wise men may go with it. And that wise men may defy it. And that fools go with it. And that fools defy it. Is your question not answered?

TEACHER: How is it answered?

SOCRATES: Why, by saying that the rebellion of a wise man is wise and that the rebellion of a fool is foolish.

TEACHER: I am not sure whether this is a paradox or a truism.

SOCRATES: It is neither. Whether a man shall conform or rebel is largely an accident of his temperament and his circumstances. But whether in his rebellion or conformity a man is wise or foolish, whether he knows what he is doing and why, and where he is going and how fast, and what the consequences are, what are the risks and the costs, what lies behind and ahead and in between—those are the questions on which everything depends.

TEACHER: Is there then no rule of conduct in these matters?

SOCRATES: Your Washington was willing to shed blood in order to defy the constituted authorities. Your Lincoln was willing to shed blood to uphold the constituted authorities. They have both been justified. There can be no rule of conduct. That which brave men do with wisdom lesser men make rules to justify.

John Dewey: RELIGION VERSUS THE RELIGIOUS

NEVER before in history has mankind been so much of two minds, so divided into two camps, as it is today. Religions have traditionally been allied with ideas of the supernatural, and often have been based upon explicit beliefs about it. Today there are many who hold that nothing worthy of being called religious is possible apart from the supernatural. Those who hold this belief differ in many respects. They range from those who accept the dogmas and sacraments of the Greek and Roman Catholic church as the only sure means of access to the supernatural to the theist or mild deist. Between them are the many Protestant denominations who think the Scriptures, aided by a pure conscience, are adequate avenues to supernatural truth and power. But they agree in one point: the necessity for a Supernatural Being and for an immortality that is beyond the power of nature.

The opposed group consists of those who think the advance of culture and science has completely discredited the

From John Dewey, *A Common Faith* (New Haven, Yale University Press, 1934), pp. 1–28. Reprinted by permission of Yale University Press.

supernatural and with it all religions that were allied with belief in it. But they go beyond this point. The extremists in this group believe that with elimination of the supernatural not only must historic religions be dismissed but with them everything of a religious nature. When historical knowledge has discredited the claims made for the supernatural character of the persons said to have founded historic religions; when the supernatural inspiration attributed to literatures held sacred has been riddled, and when anthropological and psychological knowledge has disclosed the all-too-human source from which religious beliefs and practices have sprung, everything religious must, they say, also go.

There is one idea held in common by these two opposite groups: identification of the religious with the supernatural. The question I shall raise in these chapters concerns the ground for and the consequences of this identification: its reasons and its value. In the discussion I shall develop another conception of the nature of the religious phase of experience, one that separates it from the supernatural and the things that have grown up about it. I shall try to show that these derivations are encumbrances and that what is genuinely religious will undergo an emancipation when it is relieved from them; that then, for the first time, the religious aspect of experience will be free to develop freely on its own account.

This view is exposed to attack from both the other camps. It goes contrary to traditional religions, including those that have the greatest hold upon the religiously minded today. The view announced will seem to them to cut the vital nerve of the religious element itself in taking away the basis upon which traditional religions and institutions have

been founded. From the other side, the position I am taking seems like a timid halfway position, a concession and compromise unworthy of thought that is thoroughgoing. It is regarded as a view entertained from mere tendermindedness, as an emotional hangover from childhood indoctrination, or even as a manifestation of a desire to avoid disapproval and curry favor.

The heart of my point, as far as I shall develop it in this first section, is that there is a difference between religion, *a* religion, and the religious; between anything that may be denoted by a noun substantive and the quality of experience that is designated by an adjective. It is not easy to find a definition of "religion" in the substantive sense that wins general acceptance. However, in the *Oxford Dictionary* I find the following: "Recognition on the part of man of some unseen higher power as having control of his destiny and as being entitled to obedience, reverence and worship."

This particular definition is less explicit in assertion of the supernatural character of the higher unseen power than are others that might be cited. It is, however, surcharged with implications having their source in ideas connected with the belief in the supernatural, characteristic of historic religions. Let us suppose that one familiar with the history of religions, including those called primitive, compares the definition with the variety of known facts and by means of the comparison sets out to determine just what the definition means. I think he will be struck by three facts that reduce the terms of the definition to such a low common denominator that little meaning is left.

He will note that the "unseen powers" referred to have been conceived in a multitude of incompatible ways. Eliminating the differences, nothing is left beyond the bare reference to something unseen and powerful. This has been conceived as the vague and undefined Mana of the Melanesians; the Kami of primitive Shintoism; the fetish of the Africans; spirits, having some human properties, that pervade natural places and animate natural forces; the ultimate and impersonal principle of Buddhism; the unmoved mover of Greek thought; the gods and semi-divine heroes of the Greek and Roman Pantheons; the personal and loving Providence of Christianity, omnipotent, and limited by a corresponding evil power; the arbitrary Will of Moslemism; the supreme legislator and judge of deism. And these are but a few of the outstanding varieties of ways in which the invisible power has been conceived.

There is no greater similarity in the ways in which obedience and reverence have been expressed. There has been worship of animals, of ghosts, of ancestors, phallic worship, as well as of a Being of dread power and of love and wisdom. Reverence has been expressed in the human sacrifices of the Peruvians and Aztecs; the sexual orgies of some Oriental religions; exorcisms and ablutions, or; the offering of the humble and contrite mind of the Hebrew prophet; the elaborate rituals of the Greek and Roman Churches. Not even sacrifice has been uniform; it is highly sublimated in Protestant denominations and in Moslemism. Where it has existed it has taken all kinds of forms and been directed to a great variety of powers and spirits. It has been used for expiation, for propitiation and for buying special favors. There is no conceivable purpose for which rites have not been employed.

Finally, there is no discernible unity in the moral motivations appealed to and utilized. They have been as far apart as fear of lasting torture, hope of enduring bliss in which sexual enjoyment has sometimes been a conspicuous element; mortification of the flesh and extreme asceticism; prostitution and chastity; wars to extirpate the unbeliever; persecution to convert or punish the unbeliever, and philanthropic zeal; servile acceptance of imposed dogma, along with brotherly love and aspiration for a reign of justice among men.

I have, of course, mentioned only a sparse number of the facts which fill volumes in any well-stocked library. It may be asked by those who do not like to look upon the darker side of the history of religions why the darker facts should be brought up. We all know that civilized man has a background of bestiality and superstition and that these elements are still with us. Indeed, have not some religions, including the most influential forms of Christianity, taught that the heart of man is totally corrupt? How could the course of religion in its entire sweep not be marked by practices that are shameful in their cruelty and lustfulness, and by beliefs that are degraded and intellectually incredible? What else than what we find could be expected, in the case of people having little knowledge and no secure method of knowing; with primitive institutions, and with so little control of natural forces that they lived in a constant state of fear?

I gladly admit that historic religions have been relative to the conditions of social culture in which peoples lived. Indeed, what I am concerned with is to press home the logic of this method of disposal of outgrown traits of past religions. Beliefs and practices in a religion that now prevails are by this logic relative to the present state of culture. If so much flexibility has obtained in the past regarding an unseen power, the way it affects human destiny, and the attitudes we are to take toward it, why should it be assumed that change in conception and action has now come to an end? The logic involved in getting rid of inconvenient aspects of past religions compels us to inquire how much in religions now accepted are survivals from outgrown cultures. It compels us to ask what conception of unseen powers and our relations to them would be consonant with the best achievements and aspirations of the present. It demands that in imagination we wipe the slate clean and start afresh by asking what would be the idea of the unseen, of the manner of its control over us and the ways in which reverence and obedience would be manifested, if whatever is basically religious in experience had the opportunity to express itself free from all historic encumbrances.

So we return to the elements of the definition that has been given. What boots it to accept, in defense of the universality of religion, a definition that applies equally to the most savage and degraded beliefs and practices that have related to unseen powers and to noble ideals of a religion having the greatest share of moral content? There are two points involved. One of them is that there is nothing left worth preserving in the notions of unseen powers, controlling human destiny to which obedience, reverence and worship are due, if we glide silently over the nature that has been attributed to the powers, the radically diverse ways in which they have been supposed to control human destiny, and in which submission and awe have been manifested. The other point is that when we begin to select, to choose, and say that some present ways

of thinking about the unseen powers are better than others; that the reverence shown by a free and self-respecting human being is better than the servile obedience rendered to an arbitrary power by frightened men; that we should believe that control of human destiny is exercised by a wise and loving spirit rather than by madcap ghosts or sheer force—when, I say, we begin to choose, we have entered upon a road that has not yet come to an end. We have reached a point that invites us to proceed farther.

For we are forced to acknowledge that concretely there is no such thing as religion in the singular. There is only a multitude of religions. "Religion" is a strictly collective term and the collection it stands for is not even of the kind illustrated in textbooks of logic. It has not the unity of a regiment or assembly but that of any miscellaneous aggregate. Attempts to prove the universality prove too much or too little. It is probable that religions have been universal in the sense that all the peoples we know anything about have had *a* religion. But the differences among them are so great and so shocking that any common element that can be extracted is meaningless. The idea that religion is universal proves too little in that the older apologists for Christianity seem to have been better advised than some modern ones in condemning every religion but one as an impostor, as at bottom some kind of demon worship or at any rate a superstitious figment. Choice among religions is imperative, and the necessity for choice leaves nothing of any force in the argument from universality. Moreover, when once we enter upon the road of choice, there is at once presented a possibility not yet generally realized.

For the historic increase of the ethi-

cal and ideal content of religions suggests that the process of purification
may be carried further. It indicates that
further choice is imminent in which certain values and functions in experience
may be selected. This possibility is what
I had in mind in speaking of the difference between the religious and a religion. I am not proposing a religion, but
rather the emancipation of elements and
outlooks that may be called religious.
For the moment we have a religion,
whether that of the Sioux Indian or of
Judaism or of Christianity, that moment
the ideal factors in experience that may
be called religious take on a load that is
not inherent in them, a load of current
beliefs and of institutional practices that
are irrelevant to them.

I can illustrate what I mean by a common phenomenon in contemporary life.
It is widely supposed that a person who
does not accept any religion is thereby
shown to be a non-religious person. Yet
it is conceivable that the present depression in religion is closely connected with
the fact that religions now prevent, because of their weight of historic encumbrances, the religious quality of experience from coming to consciousness and
finding the expression that is appropriate to present conditions, intellectual
and moral. I believe that such is the
case. I believe that many persons are so
repelled from what exists as a religion
by its intellectual and moral implications, that they are not even aware of
attitudes in themselves that if they came
to fruition would be genuinely religious.
I hope that this remark may help make
clear what I mean by the distinction between "religion" as a noun substantive
and "religious" as adjectival.

To be somewhat more explicit, a religion (and as I have just said there is
no such thing as religion in general) always signifies a special body of beliefs
and practices having some kind of institutional organization, loose or tight.
In contrast, the adjective "religious" denotes nothing in the way of a specifiable
entity, either institutional or as a system
of beliefs. It does not denote anything
to which one can specifically point as
one can point to this and that historic
religion or existing church. For it does
not denote anything that can exist by
itself or that can be organized into a particular and distinctive form of existence.
It denotes attitudes that may be taken
toward every object and every proposed
end or ideal.

Before, however, I develop my suggestion that realization of the distinction just made would operate to emancipate the religious quality from encumbrances that now smother or limit it, I
must refer to a position that in some respects is similar in words to the position
I have taken, but that in fact is a whole
world removed from it. I have several
times used the phrase "religious elements of experience." Now at present
there is much talk, especially in liberal
circles, of religious experience as vouch-
ing for the authenticity of certain beliefs and the desirability of certain practices, such as particular forms of prayer
and worship. It is even asserted that religious experience is the ultimate basis
of religion itself. The gulf between this
position and that which I have taken is
what I am now concerned to point out.

Those who hold to the notion that
there is a definite kind of experience
which is itself religious, by that very
fact make out of it something specific,
as a kind of experience that is marked
off from experience as aesthetic, scientific, moral, political; from experience as
companionship and friendship. But "religious" as a quality of experience sig-

nifies something that may belong to all these experiences. It is the polar opposite of some type of experience that can exist by itself. The distinction comes out clearly when it is noted that the concept of this distinct kind of experience is used to validate a belief in some special kind of object and also to justify some special kind of practice.

For there are many religionists who are now dissatisfied with the older "proofs" of the existence of God, those that go by the name of ontological, cosmological and teleological. The cause of the dissatisfaction is perhaps not so much the arguments that Kant used to show the insufficiency of these alleged proofs, as it is the growing feeling that they are too formal to offer any support to religion in action. Anyway, the dissatisfaction exists. Moreover, these religionists are moved by the rise of the experimental method in other fields. What is more natural and proper, accordingly, than that they should affirm they are just as good empiricists as anybody else—indeed, as good as the scientists themselves? As the latter rely upon certain kinds of experience to prove the existence of certain kinds of objects, so the religionists rely upon a certain kind of experience to prove the existence of the object of religion, especially the supreme object, God.

The discussion may be made more definite by introducing, at this point, a particular illustration of this type of reasoning. A writer says: "I broke down from overwork and soon came to the verge of nervous prostration. One morning after a long and sleepless night . . . I resolved to stop drawing upon myself so continuously and begin drawing upon God. I determined to set apart a quiet time every day in which I could relate my life to its ultimate source, regain

the consciousness that in God I live, move and have my being. That was thirty years ago. Since then I have had literally not one hour of darkness or despair."

This is an impressive record. I do not doubt its authenticity nor that of the experience related. It illustrates a religious aspect of experience. But it illustrates also the use of that quality to carry a superimposed load of a particular religion. For having been brought up in the Christian religion, its subject interprets it in the terms of the personal God characteristic of that religion. Taoists, Buddhists, Moslems, persons of no religion including those who reject all supernatural influence and power, have had experiences similar in their effect. Yet another author commenting upon the passage says: "The religious expert can be more sure that this God exists than he can of either the cosmological God of speculative surmise or the Christlike God involved in the validity of moral optimism," and goes on to add that such experiences "mean that God the savior, the power that gives victory over sin on certain conditions that man can fulfill, is an existent, accessible and scientifically knowable reality." It should be clear that this inference is sound only if the conditions, of whatever sort, that produce the effect are called "God." But most readers will take the inference to mean that the existence of a particular Being, of the type called "God" in the Christian religion, is proved by a method akin to that of experimental science.

In reality, the only thing that can be said to be "proved" is the existence of some complex of conditions that have operated to effect an adjustment in life, an orientation, that brings with it a sense of security and peace. The particular interpretation given to this complex of conditions is not inherent in the experience itself. It is derived from the culture with which a particular person has been imbued. A fatalist will give one name to it; a Christian Scientist another, and the one who rejects all supernatural being still another. The determining factor in the interpretation of the experience is the particular doctrinal apparatus into which a person has been inducted. The emotional deposit connected with prior teaching floods the whole situation. It may readily confer upon the experience such a peculiarly sacred preciousness that all inquiry into its causation is barred. The stable outcome is so invaluable that the cause to which it is referred is usually nothing but a reduplication of the thing that has occurred, plus some name that has acquired a deeply emotional quality.

The intent of this discussion is not to deny the genuineness of the result nor its importance in life. It is not, save incidentally, to point out the possibility of a purely naturalistic explanation of the event. My purpose is to indicate what happens when religious experience is already set aside as something *sui generis*. The actual religious quality in the experience described is the *effect* produced, the better adjustment in life and its conditions, not the manner and cause of its production. The way in which the experience operated, its function, determines its religious value. If the reorientation actually occurs, it, and the sense of security and stability accompanying it, are forces on their own account. It takes place in different persons in a multitude of ways. It is sometimes brought about by devotion to a cause; sometimes by a passage of poetry that opens a new perspective; sometimes as was the case with Spinoza—deemed an atheist in his day—through philosophical reflection.

The difference between an experience having a religious force because of what it does in and to the processes of living and religious experience as a separate kind of thing gives me occasion to refer to a previous remark. If this function were rescued through emancipation from dependence upon specific types of beliefs and practices, from those elements that constitute a religion, many individuals would find that experiences having the force of bringing about a better, deeper and more enduring adjustment in life are not so rare and infrequent as they are commonly supposed to be. They occur frequently in connection with many significant moments of living. The idea of invisible powers would take on the meaning of all the conditions of nature and human association that support and deepen the sense of values which carry one through periods of darkness and despair to such an extent that they lose their usual depressive character.

I do not suppose for many minds the dislocation of the religious from a religion is easy to effect. Tradition and custom, especially when emotionally charged, are a part of the habits that have become one with our very being. But the possibility of the transfer is demonstrated by its actuality. Let us then for the moment drop the term "religious," and ask what are the attitudes that lend deep and enduring support to the processes of living. I have, for example, used the words "adjustment" and "orientation." What do they signify?

While the words "accommodation," "adaptation," and "adjustment" are frequently employed as synonyms, attitudes exist that are so different that for the sake of clear thought they should be discriminated. There are conditions we meet that cannot be changed. If they are particular and limited, we modify our own particular attitudes in accordance with them. Thus we accommodate ourselves to changes in weather, to alterations in income when we have no other recourse. When the external conditions are lasting we become inured, habituated, or, as the process is now often called, conditioned. The two main traits of this attitude, which I should like to call *accommodation,* are that it affects *particular* modes of conduct, not the entire self, and that the process is mainly *passive.* It may, however, become general and then it becomes fatalistic resignation or submission. There are other attitudes toward the environment that are also particular but that are more active. We re-act against conditions and endeavor to change them to meet our wants and demands. Plays in a foreign language are "adapted" to meet the needs of an American audience. A house is rebuilt to suit changed conditions of the household; the telephone is invented to serve the demand for speedy communication at a distance; dry soils are irrigated so that they may bear abundant crops. Instead of accommodating ourselves to conditions, we modify conditions so that they will be accommodated to our wants and purposes. This process may be called *adaptation.*

Now both of these processes are often called by the more general name of *adjustment.* But there are also changes in ourselves in relation to the world in which we live that are much more inclusive and deep seated. They relate not to this and that want in relation to this and that condition of our surroundings, but pertain to our being in its entirety. Because of their scope, this modification of ourselves is enduring. It lasts through any amount of vicissitude of circumstances, internal and external. There is

a composing and harmonizing of the various elements of our being such that, in spite of changes in the special conditions that surround us, these conditions are also arranged, settled, in relation to us. This attitude includes a note of submission. But it is voluntary, not externally imposed; and as voluntary it is something more than a mere Stoical resolution to endure unperturbed throughout the buffetings of fortune. It is more outgoing, more ready and glad, than the latter attitude, and it is more active than the former. And in calling it voluntary, it is not meant that it depends upon a particular resolve or volition. It is a change *of* will conceived as the organic plenitude of our being, rather than any special change *in* will.

It is the claim of religions that they effect this generic and enduring change in attitude. I should like to turn the statement around and say that whenever this change takes place there is a definitely religious attitude. It is not *a* religion that brings it about, but when it occurs, from whatever cause and by whatever means, there is a religious outlook and function. As I have said before, the doctrinal or intellectual apparatus and the institutional accretions that grow up are, in a strict sense, adventitious to the intrinsic quality of such experiences. For they are affairs of the traditions of the culture with which individuals are inoculated. Mr. Santayana has connected the religious quality of experience with the imaginative, as that is expressed in poetry. "Religion and poetry," he says, "are identical in essence, and differ merely in the way in which they are attached to practical affairs. Poetry is called religion when it intervenes in life, and religion, when it merely supervenes upon life, is seen to be nothing but poetry." The difference between intervening *in* and supervening *upon* is as important as is the identity set forth. Imagination may play upon life or it may enter profoundly into it. As Mr. Santayana puts it, "poetry has a universal and a moral function," for "its highest power lies in its relevance to the ideals and purposes of life." Except as it intervenes, "all observation is observation of brute fact, all discipline is mere repression, until these facts digested and this discipline embodied in humane impulses become the starting point for a creative movement of the imagination, the firm basis for ideal constructions in society, religion, and art."

If I may make a comment upon this penetrating insight of Mr. Santayana, I would say that the difference between imagination that only supervenes and imagination that intervenes is the difference between one that completely interpenetrates all the elements of our being and one that is interwoven with only special and partial factors. There actually occurs extremely little observation of brute facts merely for the sake of the facts, just as there is little discipline that is repression and nothing but repression. Facts are usually observed with reference to some practical end and purpose, and that end is presented only imaginatively. The most repressive discipline has some end in view to which there is at least imputed an ideal quality; otherwise it is purely sadistic. But in such cases of observation and discipline imagination is limited and partial. It does not extend far; it does not permeate deeply and widely.

The connection between imagination and the harmonizing of the self is closer than is usually thought. The idea of a whole, whether of the whole personal being or of the world, is an imaginative, not a literal, idea. The limited world of our observation and reflection becomes the Universe only through imaginative extension. It cannot be apprehended in knowledge nor realized in reflection. Neither observation, thought, nor practical activity can attain that complete unification of the self which is called a whole. The *whole* self is an ideal, an imaginative projection. Hence the idea of a thoroughgoing and deep-seated harmonizing of the self with the Universe (as a name for the totality of conditions with which the self is connected) operates only through imagination—which is one reason why this composing of the self is not voluntary in the sense of an act of special volition or resolution. An "adjustment" possesses the will rather than is its express product. Religionists have been right in thinking of it as an influx from sources beyond conscious deliberation and purpose—a fact that helps explain, psychologically, why it has so generally been attributed to a supernatural source and that, perhaps, throws some light upon the reference of it by William James to unconscious factors. And it is pertinent to note that the unification of the self throughout the ceaseless flux of what it does, suffers, and achieves, cannot be attained in terms of itself. The self is always directed toward something beyond itself and so its own unification depends upon the idea of the integration of the shifting scenes of the world into that imaginative totality we call the Universe.

The intimate connection of imagination with ideal elements in experience is generally recognized. Such is not the case with respect to its connection with faith. The latter has been regarded as a substitute for knowledge, for sight. It is defined, in the Christian religion, as *evidence* of things not seen. The implication is that faith is a kind of anticipatory vision of things that are now invisible because of the limitations of our finite and erring nature. Because it is a substitute for knowledge, its material and object are intellectual in quality. As John Locke summed up the matter, faith is "assent to a proposition . . . on the credit of its proposer." Religious faith is then given to a body of propositions as true on the credit of their supernatural author, reason coming in to demonstrate the reasonableness of giving such credit. Of necessity there results the development of theologies, or bodies of systematic propositions, to make explicit in organized form the content of the propositions to which belief is attached and assent given. Given the point of view, those who hold that religion necessarily implies a theology are correct.

But belief or faith has also a moral and practical import. Even devils, according to the older theologians, believe —and tremble. A distinction was made, therefore, between "speculative" or intellectual belief and an act called "justifying" faith. Apart from any theological context, there is a difference between belief that is a conviction that some end should be supreme over conduct, and belief that some object or being exists as a truth for the intellect. Conviction in the moral sense signifies being conquered, vanquished, in our active nature by an ideal end; it signifies acknowledgment of its rightful claim over our desires and purposes. Such acknowledgment is practical, not primarily intellectual. It goes beyond evidence that can be presented to *any* possible observer. Reflection, often long and arduous, may be involved in arriving at the conviction, but the import of thought is not exhausted in discovery of evidence that can justify intellectual assent. The authority of an ideal over choice and conduct is the authority of an ideal, not of a fact, of a truth guaranteed to intellect, not of the status of the one who propounds the truth.

Such moral faith is not easy. It was questioned of old whether the Son of Man should find faith on the earth in his coming. Moral faith has been bolstered by all sorts of arguments intended to prove that its object is not ideal and that its claim upon us is not primarily moral or practical, since the ideal in question is already embedded in the existent frame of things. It is argued that the ideal is already the final reality at the heart of things that exist, and that only our senses or the corruption of our natures prevent us from apprehending its prior existential being. Starting, say, from such an idea as that justice is more than a moral ideal because it is embedded in the very make-up of the actually existent world, men have gone on to build up vast intellectual schemes, philosophies, and theologies, to prove that ideals are real not as ideals but as antecedently existing actualities. They have failed to see that in converting moral realities into matters of intellectual assent they have evinced lack of *moral* faith. Faith that something should be in existence as far as lies in our power is changed into the intellectual belief that it is already in existence. When physical existence does not bear out the assertion, the physical is subtly changed into the metaphysical. In this way, moral faith has been inextricably tied up with intellectual beliefs about the supernatural.

The tendency to convert ends of moral faith and action into articles of an intellectual creed has been furthered by a tendency of which psychologists are well aware. What we ardently desire to have thus and so, we tend to believe is already so. Desire has a powerful influence upon intellectual beliefs. Moreover, when conditions are adverse to realization of the objects of our desire—and in the case of significant ideals they are extremely adverse—it is an easy way out to assume that after all they are already embodied in the ultimate structure of what is, and that appearances to the contrary are *merely* appearances. Imagination then merely supervenes and is freed from the responsibility for intervening. Weak natures take to reverie as a refuge as strong ones do to fanaticism. Those who dissent are mourned over by the first class and converted through the use of force by the second.

What has been said does not imply that all moral faith in ideal ends is by virtue of that fact religious in quality. The religious is "morality touched by emotion" only when the ends of moral conviction arouse emotions that are not only intense but are actuated and supported by ends so inclusive that they unify the self. The inclusiveness of the end in relation to both self and the "universe" to which an inclusive self is related is indispensable. According to the best authorities, "religion" comes from a root that means being bound or tied. Originally, it meant being bound by vows to a particular way of life—as *les religieux* were monks and nuns who had assumed certain vows. The religious attitude signifies something that is bound through imagination to a *general* attitude. This comprehensive attitude, moreover, is much broader than anything indicated by "moral" in its usual sense. The quality of attitude is displayed in art, science and good citizenship.

If we apply the conception set forth to the terms of the definition earlier quoted, these terms take on a new significance. An unseen power controlling

our destiny becomes the power of an ideal. All possibilities, as possibilities, are ideal in character. The artist, scientist, citizen, parent, as far as they are actuated by the spirit of their callings, are controlled by the unseen. For all endeavor for the better is moved by faith in what is possible, not by adherence to the actual. Nor does this faith depend for its moving power upon intellectual assurance or belief that the things worked for must surely prevail and come into embodied existence. For the authority of the object to determine our attitude and conduct, the right that is given it to claim our allegiance and devotion is based on the intrinsic nature of the ideal. The outcome, given our best endeavor, is not with us. The inherent vice of all intellectual schemes of idealism is that they convert the idealism of action into a system of beliefs about antecedent reality. The character assigned this reality is so different from that which observation and reflection lead to and support that these schemes inevitably glide into alliance with the supernatural.

All religions, marked by elevated ideal quality, have dwelt upon the power of religion to introduce perspective into the piecemeal and shifting episodes of existence. Here too we need to reverse the ordinary statement and say that whatever introduces genuine perspective is religious, not that religion is something that introduces it. There can be no doubt (referring to the second element of the definition) of our dependence upon forces beyond our control. Primitive man was so impotent in the face of these forces that, especially in an unfavorable natural environment, fear became a dominant attitude, and, as the old saying goes, fear created the gods.

With increase of mechanisms of control, the element of fear has, relatively speaking, subsided. Some optimistic souls have even concluded that the forces about us are on the whole essentially benign. But every crisis, whether of the individual or of the community, reminds man of the precarious and partial nature of the control he exercises. When man, individually and collectively, has done his uttermost, conditions that at different times and places have given rise to the ideas of Fate and Fortune, of Chance and Providence, remain. It is the part of manliness to insist upon the capacity of mankind to strive to direct natural and social forces to humane ends. But unqualified absolutistic statements about the omnipotence of such endeavors reflect egoism rather than intelligent courage.

The fact that human destiny is so interwoven with forces beyond human control renders it unnecessary to suppose that dependence and the humility that accompanies it have to find the particular channel that is prescribed by traditional doctrines. What is especially significant is rather the form which the sense of dependence takes. Fear never gave stable perspective in the life of anyone. It is dispersive and withdrawing. Most religions have in fact added rites of communion to those of expiation and propitiation. For our dependence is manifested in those relations to the environment that support our undertakings and aspirations as much as it is in the defeats inflicted upon us. The essentially unreligious attitude is that which attributes human achievement and purpose to man in isolation from the world of physical nature and his fellows. Our successes are dependent upon the cooperation of nature. The sense of the dignity of human nature is as religious as is the sense of awe and reverence when it rests upon

a sense of human nature as a cooperating part of a larger whole. Natural piety is not of necessity either a fatalistic acquiescence in natural happenings or a romantic idealization of the world. It may rest upon a just sense of nature as the whole of which we are parts, while it also recognizes that we are parts that are marked by intelligence and purpose, having the capacity to strive by their aid to bring conditions into greater consonance with what is humanly desirable. Such piety is an inherent constituent of a just perspective in life.

Understanding and knowledge also enter into a perspective that is religious in quality. Faith in the continued disclosing of truth through directed cooperative human endeavor is more religious in quality than is any faith in a completed revelation. It is of course now usual to hold that revelation is not completed in the sense of being ended. But religions hold that the essential framework is settled in its significant moral features at least, and that new elements that are offered must be judged by conformity to this framework. Some fixed doctrinal apparatus is necessary for *a* religion. But faith in the possibilities of continued and rigorous inquiry does not limit access to truth to any channel or scheme of things. It does not first say that truth is universal and then add there is but one road to it. It does not depend for assurance upon subjection to any dogma or item of doctrine. It trusts that the natural interactions between man and his environment will breed more intelligence and generate more knowledge provided the scientific methods that define intelligence in operation are pushed further into the mysteries of the world, being themselves promoted and improved in the operation. There is such a thing as faith in intelligence becoming religious in quality—a fact that perhaps explains the efforts of some religionists to disparage the possibilities of intelligence as a force. They properly feel such faith to be a dangerous rival.

Lives that are consciously inspired by loyalty to such ideals as have been mentioned are still comparatively infrequent to the extent of that comprehensiveness and intensity which arouse an ardor religious in function. But before we infer the incompetency of such ideals and of the actions they inspire, we should at least ask ourselves how much of the existing situation is due to the fact that the religious factors of experience have been drafted into supernatural channels and thereby loaded with irrelevant encumbrances. A body of beliefs and practices that are apart from the common and natural relations of mankind must, in the degree in which it is influential, weaken and sap the force of the possibilities inherent in such relations. Here lies one aspect of the emancipation of the religious from religion.

Any activity pursued in behalf of an ideal end against obstacles and in spite of threats of personal loss because of conviction of its general and enduring value is religious in quality. Many a person, inquirer, artist, philanthropist, citizen, men and women in the humblest walks of life, have achieved, without presumption and without display, such unification of themselves and of their relations to the conditions of existence. It remains to extend their spirit and inspiration to ever wider numbers. If I have said anything about religions and religion that seems harsh, I have said those things because of a firm belief that the claim on the part of religions to possess a monopoly of ideals and of the supernatural means by which alone, it is alleged, they can be furthered, stands in the way of the realization of distinctively religious values inherent in natural experience. For that reason, if for no other, I should be sorry if any were misled by the frequency with which I have employed the adjective "religious" to conceive of what I have said as a disguised apology for what have passed as religions. The opposition between religious values as I conceive them and religions is not to be bridged. Just because the release of these values is so important, their identification with the creeds and cults of religions must be dissolved.

Walter M. Horton : THE NEW ORTHODOXY

TO the average college-trained American, church-goer or not, "orthodoxy" means "fundamentalism." And since that memorable occasion when fundamentalism took its stand, Canute-like, with William Jennings Bryan at Dayton, Tennessee, defying the sea of science to advance another inch, our college man is very likely to be convinced that only a rustic ignoramus can be truly orthodox. (So, in the declining days of the Roman Empire, it was only the *pagani*, the ignorant country-men, who clung to their faith in the old Olympian gods.) Imagine his

Walter M. Horton, "The New Orthodoxy," *The American Scholar*, Vol. 7, No. 1, Winter, 1938, pp. 3–11. Reprinted by permission of *The American Scholar*.

bewilderment then when he hears that many of the younger preachers and theologians—some of whom had their university course at Princeton or Harvard and their theological course in schools as pronouncedly liberal as Chicago Divinity School or Union Seminary—are now beginning to go "orthodox"! Imagine his distress when he is told that Professor Reinhold Niebuhr, whose shrewd analyses of current social issues have won his respect, is now bearing "theologically to the right" and (some say) heading full steam for orthodoxy!

The news is correct in the main though somewhat misleading unless rightly interpreted. Active young minds in the churches and seminaries *are* beginning to show a marked conservative trend. A generation ago young preachers and theological students were likely to be in revolt against traditional Christian theology wherever it came into collision with modern scientific or philosophical ideas. Today they are still in revolt—the perpetual prerogative of youth—but they are in revolt against liberalism. The statement is not, of course, true without qualification. In many churches and seminaries, especially in the South, the conflict between fundamentalism and liberalism still goes on and youth is on the liberal side. But precisely where the victory of liberal Christianity has been most complete, in the Northern urban centers, the reaction against it is most pronounced and the trend toward orthodoxy most unmistakable.

This new conservative movement is essentially different from fundamentalism. Fundamentalism was pre-modernistic; the new orthodoxy is post-modernistic. Fundamentalism was a defensive movement, designed to protect the historic "deposit of faith" against the destructive inroads of its modern environ-

ment; the new orthodoxy is an aggressive pioneering movement, already adjusted to its modern environment but pushing on through the increasingly arid desert of modern existence with the help of ancient maps and ancient travelers' songs— the rediscovered legacy of an "Eternal People" whose "Eternal Road" has often taken them through that self-same wilderness.

The new orthodoxy has only recently appeared in America but it has flourished for fifteen years in Continental Europe. American delegates to the church unity conferences which met at Oxford and Edinburgh this summer became aware of its pervasive influence when they encountered opposition of "the Continentals" on every major issue. At first with amusement or indignation, then with some respect, they were repeatedly obliged to listen to a point of view in which the German and Scandinavian Lutherans, the French and Dutch Calvinists and the Eastern Orthodox seemed all substantially at one, but which was as remote from the "Anglo-Saxon" (British or American) position as Timbuktoo from Kalamazoo.

Sometimes this Continental point of view was described as "Barthian" by its American critics. This was undoubtedly a misnomer. Most of the Continentals would have refused—perhaps with some heat—to be called followers of Karl Barth; and he himself had he been present might have unchurched the great majority of them. Yet somehow the Continental delegation did look "Barthian" to the Americans and might properly be called Barthian in a relative sense as Canada is British to the Americans and American to the British. For Barth is the pioneer of the new orthodoxy and its most extreme representative. Few accept his teachings *in toto* but all Europe feels the pull of his influence. The easiest way to define any European theologian's position is to ask, "Where does he stand in relation to Barth?"

Karl Barth is not (like Bishop Manning) a constitutional conservative. With quizzical eyes peering out from behind thick lenses and a leering, lopsided grin he looks more like a Bolshevik than like an ecclesiastic, and his appearance is not deceptive. Before the World War he was what used to be called an "advanced" thinker: A Christian Socialist, a sharp critic of the modern *bourgeois* church, and a theological liberal of the neo-Kantian variety, trained under Wilhelm Herrmann at Marburg. He is still a Socialist in politics and his suspicion of the decadence of the modern church has grown to prophetic certainty, but he does not identify the Socialist Utopia with the Kingdom of God and in theology he has pushed beyond liberalism, through radical skepticism, to a militant, revolutionary orthodoxy reminiscent of Luther and Calvin.

It was during the War, as minister of a little Reformed church in northwest Switzerland, that Barth passed through the radical crisis which made him orthodox. Trying to preach his liberal social gospel in wartime, while big guns over the horizon in Alsace punctuated his exhortations with ironical comments, he was thrown, he tells us, into a profound "embarrassment." Here were people pathetically expectant, longing to be assured of the reality of God in a world suddenly gone mad. Here was a Book the burden of whose every page was the reality of God. And here stood he, supposed to preach the Word of God to these people but unable to believe in his own sermons!

One thing he found he could no longer do with honest conviction—explain God by identifying him with any contemporary social movement or tendency or with anything temporal or human. Hegel might do that, Utopian Socialists might do that, but Kierkegaard and current events had conspired to remove the scales from Barth's eyes. Taught by the great Danish critic, whose works had such a vogue in the German-speaking world during the War, he learned to doubt whether the anti-theses of human society were really leading on toward a glorious divine synthesis which would comprehend all tragic differences in some equable and rational "Both . . . and." Human life, as he observed it and as he found it magnificently analyzed in Dostoievsky's novels, seemed to be an insoluble paradox, a question without an answer. Both the Christian Church and the Socialist party seemed to be rushing to perdition rather than marching toward the Millennium. A God one could trust and reverence must be wholly above and beyond all this. There must be, as Kierkegaard said, an "infinite qualitative difference" between the temporal and the eternal.

Such pessimism as this was no doubt irreligious according to liberal Christian notions, but as Barth despairingly searched the Scriptures it struck him that a certain pessimism about human affairs was characteristic of their teachings, and when he turned to the Biblical commentaries of Luther and Calvin he was pleased to discover that these men of faith viewed the secular scene pretty much as he did. Perhaps after all it was not wrong to be "embarrassed" when one attempted to make God intelligible in terms of contemporary social movements; perhaps a God who could be discovered on the human plane would not be God; perhaps "embarrassment," inability to talk without involvement in verbal contradictions and rational paradoxes, was something one was *bound* to experience in the presence of the true and living God who is "wholly other" (*totaliter aliter*) than all our ideas of him. Perhaps theology itself is but "the description of this embarrassment." This was Barth's first great theological insight and it has remained fundamental for him.[1]

The book which brought Barth to the attention of the world was his *Commentary on the Epistle to the Romans*, which has passed through many editions and radical revisions since it first appeared in 1918. It is a strange book, full of the most astonishing paradoxes—deliberately so, since Barth is convinced that wherever God impinges upon human life he reveals himself in some apparent contradiction; death that is life, despair that is hope, an insoluble enigma which is its own triumphant answer. It is not a conventionally pious book, for in the name of God Barth heaps his scorn upon religion and the church—above all upon that liberal Christianity which fails to see that "one can *not* speak of God simply by speaking of man in a loud voice." [2] But for all this, it is a religiously stirring book, for Barth has now found in the Bible what he regards as the absolute Word of God, lifted high above all the perishable counsels of men. This does not mean that he has turned his back upon the critical, scientific study of the Bible or failed to recognize the human and fallible elements in the teachings of the prophets and apostles. He has no animus against the "higher criticism"; but for him the real task of Biblical interpretation begins where the critic's task ends, where the interpreter stops to listen for the Word which the God who produced the Bible has to speak to our own time. Barth's *Romans*, coming after a generation of cool, objective Biblical scholarship, gave the theological world a sudden shock, for it dared to translate Paul's epistle to the Romans into a special-delivery letter from God to the 20th century.

This crisis in the life of Karl Barth is typical of the crisis through which multitudes of Europeans—some independently, some stimulated by his leadership—have been passing in the post-war era. They have turned back from liberal Christianity toward more classical sources of inspiration because they have become convinced that modern civilization, with all its indubitable achievements, is now in a blind alley from which we must back out before we can hope to go ahead again. They have abandoned the liberal Christian emphasis upon the indwelling ("immanence") of God in the world and in man because God no longer appears to them as the Patron of modern humanistic culture but as its Adversary and Judge. In this general attitude Barth is at one not only with "Barthians" who accept his theology but also with many of his Protestant critics and even with Roman Catholic and Eastern Orthodox thinkers. Whether we listen to Maritain the Catholic on *Freedom in the Modern World* or Berdyaev the Russian Orthodox on *The Fate of Man in the Modern World* or Barth's Protestant antagonist Schweitzer on *The Decay and Restoration of Civilization* we always get the same diagnosis: modern man, having attempted to make himself the center of the universe, has fallen victim to his own mechanical ingenuity and unless he can find a new center for his existence above and beyond himself, in God, his mechanized civilization is doomed to suffer the fate described in *The Decline of the West*.

---

[1] See Barth, *The Word of God and the Word of Man*, trans. Douglas Horton, pp. 100, 101.
[2] *Ibid.*, p. 198.

Unanimity vanishes, of course, when these thinkers pass from criticism to construction. All agree that a strategic retreat to some impregnable fortress of Christian faith is necessary but each builds his fortress at a different spot in accordance with the pattern of the Christian tradition to which he adheres. Maritain calls us back to St. Thomas, Berdyaev to the mystics and philosophers of the Eastern Church, Barth to the Protestant Reformers and their *sola Scriptura, soli Deo gloria,* and Albert Schweitzer, less radically anti-modern, calls us back to the Christian humanitarianism of the Age of the Enlightenment.

Barth is less influential and representative on this constructive side of the new orthodoxy than on its critical side. His contempt for all that is merely human or temporal, his distrust of human reason as an avenue of approach to God, are so thoroughgoing that he is left without any intellectual cement wherewith to hold the jagged fragments of his faith together or to build a bridge between faith and knowledge. He has lately parted company with his most able disciple, Emil Brunner, because Brunner made room in his theology for a real though incomplete knowledge of God derived from direct observation of nature and human society; and others have left him for similar reasons.

Unless all signs fail, the future development of the new orthodoxy is going to follow Brunner's lead rather than Barth's. One cannot imagine the Catholic or Eastern Orthodox Churches giving up their rational *praeambula fidei* whereby the acceptance of superhuman revelation becomes itself a reasonable act. Still less can one expect theologians trained in the Liberal Protestant tradition to turn their backs collectively upon philosophic reason as a guide to the knowledge of God. What one may expect and what seems to be occurring is a shift of base in philosophy—from idealistic optimism and "world-affirmation" to realistic pessimism and "world-denial." As the monks in medieval Europe withdrew to their monasteries, where they treasured and studied the records of Christian antiquity and prayed to a God who was above the battle that raged around their walls, so the modern church, in Europe, is beginning to interiorize her life, to live less on surrounding culture than on her own precious heritage, and to pin her faith to a transcendent God who will survive the coming doom of Western civilization.

What will America do about the new orthodoxy? So far she has done very little. Our relative peace and isolation make it hard to believe on this side of the water, that European thinkers are really in earnest when they talk about the impending doom of civilization and the inability of man to avert it by his own efforts. Only quite recently, during the economic depression, did the American mind begin to lose something of its ingrained optimism and consider whether there might not be something really and basically wrong with the world. It was during this period that Reinhold Niebuhr rose to a position of commanding influence in the theological world. In him we probably have the best measuring-rod that could be devised to test the extent of our response to the new orthodoxy and the distance which divides it from yesterday's fundamentalism and modernism.

Like his friend Paul Tillich—who has now become his colleague at Union Seminary—Niebuhr has always lived "on the boundary" between rival currents of thought.[3] A German-American, well-

[3] See Tillich, *The Interpretation of History,* Part I, "On the Boundary: an autobiographical

grounded in the conservative traditions of the Lutheran and Reformed Churches but equally versed in the political philosophy of John Dewey and the intricacies of the American labor movement, he has for years been reading Continental theology and applying it to the American scene. This practice has long since led him to view his native America with a detached and somewhat ironical gaze. It has also led him to criticize the Continental point of view from the American angle. The result—to employ his favorite term—has been the development of a powerful "tension" in his mind, where Europe and America are perpetually tugging in opposite directions. So long as America continues to tug he will never go completely orthodox in the Barthian sense. So long as Europe continues to tug he will never cease to pull American theology toward a deeper appreciation of the truth in orthodoxy. In all his recent books, orthodoxy and liberalism are made to carry on a continuous process of mutual criticism which should be for the ultimate benefit of both. The verdict in this internal debate would run like this: Liberal Christianity, especially in its American form, has been unrealistic and romantic in its estimate of the difficulties which beset mankind. It has believed it possible to realize the Kingdom of God on earth by collective moral effort, forgetting that society is largely made up of sinners and has a way of corrupting even the virtues of saints through collective self-deception. Orthodox Christianity, notably in its European form, has been so pessimistic about human nature, so

transcendental in its view of God, that it has tended to make all moral distinctions vanish in a universal condemnation of sin-in-general, thus cutting the nerve of effort and rendering history meaningless. Actually we face a world where the Christian Gospel is "relevant" at every moment but never finally reaches its goal. "No absolute limit can be placed upon the degree to which human society may yet approximate the ideal. But it is certain that every achievement will remain in the realm of approximation." [4]

This verdict of Niebuhr's is comparable at many points with the verdict which British theology—closer to the Continent than we are—has already reached in its discussion of the new orthodoxy. Led by Dean Inge and others, contemporary British theology has abandoned the Utopian expectation of reaching the Kingdom of Heaven on earth by cooperative human effort; it conceives of history as a perpetual struggle between a transcendent divine Will and a creative process dependent on that Will but capable of resisting it to the point of self-destruction. With British common sense, however, it insists upon the possibility of tracing the hand of God even in the history of his rebellious creatures and continues to hope for divine victories in this earthly sphere, victories of such a quality that man may learn from them to know the taste of eternity in the midst of time. [5]

If such an attitude is remote from the modernism which floats blissfully down the stream of contemporary civilization, confident of the divinity, yea, the Christlikeness of its prevailing currents and the happiness of the condition toward which

---

sketch." Tillich, like Barth, has been driven from his professorship in Germany by the opposition of the Nazis. A severe critic of Barth, he nevertheless resembles him in his pessimism about contemporary society and his transcendental conception of God—"the Unconditioned,"

[4] *An Interpretation of Christian Ethics*, p. 111.
[5] For an interpretation of the general trend of British theology see *Contemporary English Theology* by the author of this article.

it is tending, it is equally remote from the fundamentalism which identifies the Word of God with an ancient Book. For Niebuhr (as indeed for Barth himself, with all his anti-modernism) the Word of God is something contemporaneous, or rather something eternal, which impinges upon our age through a human and fallible historic medium. Literal faith in the *ipsissima verba* of Scripture is a form of idolatry which God will punish as He will punish the idolatrous State-worship of our nationalistic contemporaries. But let the words of Scripture be taken as what Niebuhr calls "myths" and Barth calls "tokens"—symbolic expressions of truths too transcendent for human science to grasp, on which nevertheless our

human fate depends—and they will lead us back to a fresh appreciation of Christian orthodoxy.

In its great ages orthodoxy has not stifled intelligence or shackled the present to an archaic past. It has been a living tradition, perpetually reborn through reapplication to the needs and problems of each new generation, perpetually confirmed by the disasters which ensue when humanity departs from it. In G. K. Chesterton's famous figure, orthodoxy careens down the pathway of the centuries like a charioteer, reeling but erect, spilling out heretics and extremists to the right and left but managing by the grace of God to maintain its balance.

Reinhold Niebuhr: THE TRUTH IN MYTHS

IN the lexicon of the average modern, particularly in America, a myth is a piece of fiction, usually inherited from the childhood of the race. The scientific outlook of our mature culture has supposedly invalidated the truth value of these primitive stories in which gods and devils, nymphs and satyrs, fairies and witches are portrayed in actions and attitudes which partly transcend and partly conform to human limitations. They are regarded as the opulent fruits of an infantile imagination which are bound to wither under the sober discipline of a developed intelligence. Science has displaced mythology. A careful observation of the detailed phenomena of life and history yields more credible explanations of life's mysteries than these fanciful accounts of the origin of life or the

genesis of evil or these fantastic pictures of the universe. When we have the conception of evolution we do not need the story of creation, and when we see man's slow ascent toward the ideal we have no place for a mythical "fall" to account for the origin of evil in the world. The reign of law revealed by science invalidates the miracles which abound in all religions; and the insight into, and power over, his own future given to the modern man through his intelligence frees him of the need to seek salvation in the myths of religion. Such are the convictions which belong to the unquestioned certainties of the modern man.

Since mythical elements are irrevocably enshrined in the canons of all religions it has become the fashion of modern religion to defend itself against the

From Reinhold Niebuhr *et al.*, *The Nature of Religious Experience: Essays in Honor of Clyde Macintosh* (New York, Harper and Brothers, 1937), pp. 117–123, 125–132, 133–135. Reprinted by permission.

criticisms of science by laborious reinterpretations of its central affirmations with the purpose of sloughing off the mythical elements, apologizing for them as inevitable concepts of infantile cultures, and extracting the perennially valid truths from these husks of the past. Unfortunately the protagonists of modern religion usually fail to placate the devotees of the scientific method by these diligent but not too dignified labors. They are met by the contemptuous suggestion that they have been merely insinuating new meanings into ancient phrases, and that they have gained nothing for their pains but what might have been secured more simply by a scientific analysis of the known facts of life and existence. If science has the final word and authority about life, as many of those theologians who have been most anxious to adjust religion to the scientific world view have assumed, this suggestion is plausible enough. Indeed some of the supposedly abiding truths which have been distilled from ancient myths by this process of reinterpretation have lost their religious essence so completely, have been flattened and deflated to such a degree in the process of adaptation, that the charge of the empiricists and naturalists seems perfectly justified.

The modern protagonists of religion made the mistake of retreating too far and too quickly when the exigencies of the cultural situation demanded a retreat. Their error was to disavow permanent myth with primitive myth. Religion had no right to insist on the scientific accuracy of its mythical heritage. From this position a retreat was necessary. That part of mythology which is derived from pre-scientific thought, which does not understand the causal relations in the natural and historical world, must naturally be sacrificed in a scientific age. But there is a permanent as well as a primitive myth in every great mythical heritage. This deals with aspects of reality which are supra-scientific rather than pre-scientific. Modernistic religion has been so thin on the whole because it did not understand this distinction and thus sacrificed what is abiding with what is primitive in religious myth.

What are the aspects of reality which can be stated only in mythical terms?

The most obvious aspect of reality which can not be comprehended in terms of scientific concepts is the aspect of value. It is true that the value of things for a particular individual can always be stated in terms of aesthetic myths. The aesthetic myth (such as "Hail to thee, blithe Spirit! Bird thou never wert," in Shelley's ode "To a Skylark") makes no claim about the ultimate value of a thing in a total scheme of purpose. It merely asserts value in terms of the moods and purposes of an individual in a given instance. The purely aesthetic and non-religious myth is therefore sceptical about values in the ultimate sense. "Poetry," declares Santayana, "is religion which is no longer believed." The aesthetic myth becomes transmuted into a religious myth when it seeks to comprehend facts and occurrences in terms of their organic relation to the whole conceived in teleological terms. For only if things are related to each other organically in a total meaningful existence can it be claimed that they have value. Religion, to transpose Santayana's phrase, is poetry which is believed. Religion seeks mythically to grasp life in its unity and wholeness. This unity and wholeness can never be expressed in terms of complete rationality; for reason only observes and deduces. What it observes is concrete reality in its multifarious forms. Its deductions are based upon the sequences which it observes in nature and history. But these sequences reveal nothing of the internal unity in all organic growth. For this reason scientific descriptions of reality always tend to a mechanistic interpretation of it. The facts of organic growth can be comprehended and described only by mythically transferring the inner unity of the human consciousness (where unity is directly experienced and apprehended) to the external world. A certain amount of primitive myth is always involved in this process (its analogy to animism of primitive mythology is apparent). But it is also permanent myth in the sense that it is permanently valid, since reality is actually organic and not mechanical in its processes.

A full analysis of the organic aspect of life reveals another quality of existence which can not be comprehended in terms of rationality and which might be defined as the dimension of depth in existence. If the relatedness of things to each other is more than mechanical, the source of their unity lies beyond, behind and above the observable phenomena. "The world of things as they are," to quote Professor William P. Montague, "is not self-explanatory; it bears the earmarks, if not of a manufactured product, at least of a thing which has been derived from something other than itself." Not only the secret of its unity but of its growth (the emergence of novelty) lies beyond itself. Sciences may carefully observe certain processes of life and history and describe how or under what concatenation of circumstances certain forms, biological or social, were transmuted into other forms. But it can only describe these processes after the fact, and it is forced to treat each new emergent as following necessarily from the forces which immediately preceded it. It is, therefore, constantly tempted to commit the logi-

cal fallacy of *post hoc; ergo propter hoc.* It is, in short, compelled to deny the idea of creation.

The idea of creation is a typical mythical idea. It relates the source of life to observable life in terms which defy rationality. The primitive myth speaks of God making man out of clay, and breathing the breath of life into him. But the idea of creation remains mythical even when the primitive myth is discarded. If the myth is completely rationalized the creator becomes the first cause. Inasfar as he is merely a cause, among many causes, creation is denied and every new fact in history is explained in terms of previous facts. Inasfar as he is a uniquely first cause the limits of logic in dealing with the problem of causation in history are recognized but the recognition is left in negative form. Thus when religion refuses to yield the idea of creation to the idea of evolution it is following an instinct for the truth. When, as has been frequently the case in modern religion, it apologetically declares that nothing but a difference in terminology is involved ("Some call it evolution and others call it God") it is erroneously yielding to the prejudices of a scientific age.

The myth of creation not only expresses dynamic and organic qualities in reality which can not be stated in rational terms, but paradoxical qualities which elude the canons of logic. The dimension of depth in life contains such a paradox. All life and existence in its concrete forms suggests not only sources but possibilities beyond itself. These possibilities must be implied in the source or they would not be true possibilities. God is in other words both the ultimate ground of reality and its ultimate goal. "Religion," to quote Professor Montague in a revealing phrase, ". . . is the acceptance of the momentous possibility—that what is highest in spirit is also deepest in nature, that the ideal and the real are at least to some extent identified, not merely evanescently in our own lives but in the universe itself." [1] The myth of creation, in which God is neither identified with the historical world nor separated from it, offers the basis upon which all theologies are built in which God is conceived as both the ground and the ultimate fulfillment of a meaningful world, as both the creator and the judge of historical existence. This paradox is really the only ground of an effective ethic because it alone harmonizes ethical and metaphysical interests and gives us a picture of a world which is really a universe, but not so unqualifiedly a meaningful world as to obscure the fact of evil and the possibility of a dynamic ethics. Every dynamic ethics depends upon the dimension of depth in life and upon a description of this dimension, which neither equates the metrical and mechanistic aspects of concrete existence with meaning and value, nor completely separates the world of value and ideals from the facts of concrete existence.

Efforts to describe the unity and meaningfulness of the world and existence in purely rational terms must ultimately choose between a metaphysics which inclines to monistic idealism (and may finally degenerate into a dualism) or a science which inclines to a mechanistic monism. Most of the modern efforts to arrive at a unified picture of life and reality have been under the direct influence of science rather than metaphysics. When science disavows both myth and metaphysics it has only two alternatives in its attempt to construct a total world picture. It may picture the world

[1] Montague, William Pepperell, *Belief Unbound,* p. 6.

and life as a mechanism, held together by the mechanical processes which it believes to have discovered by its observations. But there is only superficial unity and no meaningfulness in such a world. There is no place in it for the kind of vital and organic unity which the self experiences in its own self-consciousness. The logical ultimate of such a world view is found in behavioristic psychology which denies the unity of consciousness as a reality. But such an ultimate is self-destructive because it invalidates the truth value of everything discovered by the conscious self about the world in which it lives. It is furthermore destructive of human vitality because it is impossible to live with zest if no purposes can be found worthy of our striving. A purely mechanical world is bereft of purpose and meaningfulness.

The other alternative (more generally followed) is to introduce mythical and transcendent elements covertly (usually unconsciously) into the supposedly scientific accounts of life and history. Our modern culture has maintained its spiritual life by such a covert myth: the idea of progress. It is possible to speak of progress in interpreting the endless changes of life only if some measuring rod of value can be found with which to gauge the process. But the rod must not be a part of the process. It must transcend it. The rod taken by modern culture has usually been some ethical ideal, inherited from religion. The confidence that the processes of nature support and contribute to the victory of this ethical ideal is really a rationalized version of the Christian myth of salvation. Unfortunately it is more optimistic and really less credible than the Christian myth. It derives its credulous optimism from the fact that it sacrificed the primary myth of creation prematurely and thus identifies the processes of history too uncritically with the transcendent ideal implied in these processes. It is only through the myth of creation that it is possible to assert both the meaningfulness of life and the fact of evil. To say that God created the world is to assert its meaningfulness; and to distinguish between the creator and his creation is to make a place for the reality of evil in the inevitable relativities of time and history. . . .

Neither the vital thrust of life, nor its organic unities, nor its disharmonies, nor its highest possibilities can be expressed in terms of logic and rational consistency. The dynamic and creative energy of life can be described but not comprehended by reason. The unities of life are organic, and reason can only logically assemble after analytically dividing, thus reducing the organic to a mechanical unity. The disharmonies of life are paradoxically related to its harmonies, as mechanism is paradoxically related to the world of meaning and purpose and every rational scheme of coherence fails to do justice to the tragic realities of evil and to its paradoxical relation with the good.

The dimension of depth in existence has thus far been dealt with only as if it were a fact in the world external to man. But it is really man, with his capacity of transcending the world and transcending himself, who comprehends this depth in existence, and feels it within himself. Man is a creature of both necessity and freedom. He is inserted in the mechanisms of nature and bound by them. Yet he also gains freedom over them by his capacity to envisage purposes and ideals more inclusive than those to which he is driven by nature's impulses. For him the problem of evil is therefore also a problem of sin. His freedom endows him with responsibility and his responsibility spells

guilt. The impulse of nature is not evil in the beast because it has no alternatives. But every human action is a choice between alternatives. An external description of the act may prove that a particular action was inevitable because a dominant impulse or set of forces actuated it. But an internal description of an act of choice can never escape a comparison between the act and a higher possibility. It is for this reason that religion, which has a grasp of this dimension of depth, deals with the fact of sin, while science, with its external descriptions, always inclines to deny the reality of sin and the fact of human responsibility.

In spite of the fact that the responsibility of freedom enters into every moral act, purely moralistic descriptions of human sin are as erroneous as purely deterministic and external description of human conduct. The relation of man to freedom and to mechanism is paradoxical. His conscious self is never in complete control of the mechanisms of impulse with which nature has endowed him. Yet it is in sufficient control not only to check these impulses in the interest of a more inclusive purpose but to interfere with the harmony of natural impulses, and to transmute the harmless impulses of nature into demonic lusts and imperialistic purposes. It is, in other words, the nature of human sin that it arises at the juncture of nature and spirit and is as much the corruption of nature by spirit as the corruption of spirit by nature.

All this is darkly expressed in the myth of the fall in Christian theology, much more adequately than in rational explanations of human evil. In explanations which achieve full rational coherence, evil is either attributed to the ultimate source of being (as in various forms of monism), in which case the reality of evil is really denied; or it is attributed to the world of matter, nature and historical concretion (as in various forms of dualism) in which case the fall is equated with creation (in gnosticism for instance), and impulses of nature are regarded as the source of evil while the direction of mind is regarded as the source of all good. Modern liberalism, with its confidence in increasing virtue through increasing control of reason over impulse, is a particularly naive version of this kind of dualism, though liberalism rests upon a metaphysical foundation of naturalistic monism. Against these rationalistic versions the myth of the fall expresses these ideas: that an element of human perversity is always involved in human sin since a degree of freedom enters into every human action; that nevertheless sin is inevitable since all men are inserted into the paradoxical relation of freedom and mechanism and can not escape the possibility of destroying the harmony of nature without achieving the ultimate harmony of spirit; and, finally, that this inevitability is not to be attributed merely to the fact of nature, finiteness and the world of concrete mechanism and physical impulse. The fact that the fall came after creation, and is not synonymous or contemporaneous with it, in the Jewish-Christian myth, has always saved Christian orthodoxy from falling into dualistic heresies, no matter how strongly tempted it has been in various periods of Christian history.[2] Modern theology has been scornful of the doctrine of original sin (a corollary of the myth of the fall in Christian orthodoxy), because in its moralism and optimism it imagined the possibility of escape from the paradoxical

human situation of finiteness and freedom. Orthodoxy, leaning upon mythical insights, has been truer to the facts of the total human situation upon this point. The real situation is that man's very self-consciousness and capacity for self-transcendence is not only the prerequisite of his morality but the fateful and inevitable cause of his sin. It is because man can transcend nature and himself that he is able to conceive of himself as the center of all life and the clue to the meaning of existence. It is this monstrous pretension of his egoism, the root of all imperialism and human cruelty, which is the very essence of sin. To recognize all this is not to accept the story of the fall as history. The modern dialectical theology of Germany calls it *Urgeschichte,* and that is perhaps as good a term as any. Whenever orthodoxy insists upon the literal truth of such myths it makes a bad historical science out of true religious insights. It fails to distinguish between what is primitive and what is permanent, what is pre-scientific and what is supra-scientific in great myths.

The religious myths of salvation spring from the same necessity as the myths of creation and the fall. The modern man thinks himself emancipated from the need of religious assurances of salvation. They seem to him theological and unreal. The only redemption in which he believes is moral redemption, the actual conquest of evil by the good. But he can regard the problem of salvation as so simple only because he has equated evil and sin with ignorance. Once the element of perversity in evil is recognized, salvation in the full sense is possible only if the will is changed (conversion), and if the guilt of the past is pardoned. In all genuine religious experiences of salvation there is a sense of new moral power and an assurance of pardon. This

[2] See, for an historical elaboration of this thesis, Williams, N. P., *The Idea of The Fall and of Original Sin.*

is in other words a transaction between a transcendent God, who is not bound by the iron laws of necessity in history, and a transcendent self, which also stands above these laws both in the evil that it has committed and in the moral will by which it overcomes its previous perversity. If sin is not merely imperfection and weakness but an act of the will, reconciliation is possible only through an act of the will of the Divine; and this can be revealed only if divine forgiveness achieves some form and symbol in history (the Incarnation). The absurdity of theologies which try to define the two natures of Christ and to distinguish between the temporal and the eternal in the mythical God-man, proves how impossible it is to bring essential myth into the categories of rationality. A completely rationalized myth loses its virtue because it ceases to point to the realm of transcendence beyond history, or, pointing to it, fails to express the organic and paradoxical relationship between the conditioned and the unconditioned. That is why, as Clutton-Brock observed, religion is forced to tell many little lies in the interest of a great truth, while science inclines to tell many little truths in the interest of a great lie. The great truth in the interest of which many little lies are told is that life and history have meaning and that the source and the fulfillment of that meaning lie beyond history. The great lie in the interest of which science tells many little truths is that spatio-temporal realities are self-contained and self-explanatory and that a scientific description of sequences is an adequate analysis of causes.

It has been previously suggested that the myths of art are related to those of religion. It could be claimed, in further elaboration of this thesis, that great art is bound to be religious; for great art is more than the objectivization of a particular sentiment or sense of meaning. It is a symbolization of the universal in the particular, to use Goethe's definition of great art. Its analyses of particular situations or its objectivizations of particular sentiments contain suggestions of the total human situation. But the very quality in them which points to the universal or the transcendent makes them something more and less than a scientific description of the facts.

A portrait is mythical as compared with the scientific exactitude of a photograph. Though a wise photographer will try to catch the permanent and significant rather than the passing mood of his subject he is always limited by the physical facts. The artist, on the other hand, falsifies some of the physical details in order to arrive at a symbolic expression of the total character of his subject, this total character being a transcendent fact which is never completely embodied in any given moment of the subject's existence. A really great portrait will go beyond this and symbolize not only the transcendent personality of the subject, but will contain suggestions of a universal human mood. The artistic licence of the artist belongs in the same category as the artistic licence of religion. In both cases it is subject to abuses. The artist may falsify reality and produce a caricature of his subject rather than a true portrait; and religious myths may falsify the facts of history and experience. But at their best, both artist and prophet reveal the heights and depths of human experience by picturing the surface with something more and less than scientific exactness.

Critics of Greek literature are agreed that Euripides's *Electra* is inferior to the *Choephori* of Aeschylus and the *Electra* of Sophocles, all three dramas dealing with the same theme, the vengeance of Orestes upon his mother. But the prejudices of modern culture have made it difficult to give the reason for this inferiority as simply as it might be given. Euripides is the secularist among the three great dramatists. Under his pen the great myths are naturalized and secularized so that human actions and attitudes become the inevitable causes and consequences of succeeding and preceding actions. He thus dissipates the power of Greek tragedy; for at its best it fills us with a sense of the beauty and terror of life by suggesting that human destinies are woven by forces vaster than human wills. Greek drama at its best lies close to its source: Dionysiac religion. Like all great art, it shares with religion the intention and the power to illumine the facts of life and the course of history by pointing to sources of meaning which lie beyond the facts we see and the history we experience.

The ultimate problem of myth is always the problem of God. Myths may begin by picturing good and evil spirits and by personalizing the forces of wind and water, of sun and moon and the starry heavens. Since every natural phenomenon can be explained in terms of a preceding one the myth becomes useless when science discovers the chain of causation. But meanwhile mythical knowledge has been driven from the effort to seek the transcendent cause behind each phenomenon to the search after the ultimate source of the meaning of all existence.

The approach to the transcendent source of meaning confronts us with a problem which seems practically insoluble. If the meaningfulness of life points to a source beyond itself, how is it possible to say anything about that transcendence, and how can anything

that may be said be verified as true? "The vision into the Absolute," declares Professor Morris Cohen, "is either into a fathomless depth in which no distinctions are visible or into a fulness of being that exceeds our human comprehension." Mysticism has usually insisted on the distinctionless aspect of the transcendent. By seeking the absolute through a progressive elimination of temporal distinctions it finally arrived at the knowledge of God: but the God it found was emptiness and void. It could say nothing about him but that he negated the reality of significance of temporal existence. The final logic of this method is consistently expressed in Buddhism in which the ultimate is a distinctionless reality which serves only to destroy the meaning of temporal existence. Something of the same logic is to be found in all mystic asceticism. Thus the search after meaning becomes self-devouring. An ultimate source of meaning is found about which nothing can be said except that it destroys the meaning of mundane existence. . . .

The inadequacy of purely rational approaches invariably forces a return to a purer mythical approach in which the transcendent is defined and ceases to be mere emptiness, but is defined in terms which insist that it is more (and therefore less) than mere totality. But the problem of religion is how it may define God without resorting to a dogmatic acceptance of whatever mythical definition a particular historic tradition has entrusted to a certain portion of the religious community. The modern reaction against naturalism and rationalism expressed in Barthianism fails, significantly, to escape dogmatism. It is superior to the older dogmatisms of orthodox religion in that it does not insist on the scientific and rational validity of the mythical details of its tradition. The Fall and the Resurrection are not conceived as historical in its theology. But the total truth of the Biblical myth is asserted dogmatically with no effort to validate Christianity in experience against competition with other religions.

How is it possible to escape this dogmatism? It is possible only if it be realized that though human knowledge and experience always point to a source of meaning in life which transcends knowledge and experience, there are nevertheless suggestions of the character of this transcendence in experience. Great myths have actually been born out of profound experience and are constantly subject to verification by experience. It may be simplest to illustrate this point in terms of a specific religious doctrine: the Christian doctrine that God is love and that love is the highest moral ideal.

The ideal of love is not a caprice of mythology. It is not true because the Cross has revealed it. The Cross justifies itself to human faith because it symbolizes an ideal which establishes points of relevance with the deepest experiences and insights of human life.

The ideal of love can be validated as the ultimate moral ideal because it stands in a verifiable transcendent relation to all rational idealism. It is both the fulfillment and the abyss of the rational ideal of justice. Justice is the highest rational moral ideal because reason must seek to deal with human relations and moral conduct in terms of the ascertainable causes and consequences of action. A good act must be rewarded and an evil one punished. The interest of my neighbor must be guarded; but my own interests deserve protection as well. Yet all rational justice constantly sinks to something less than justice. Remedial justice fails to "do justice" to the causes

which prompted an evil act because it is ignorant of the operations of mind and conscience in that secret place where actions are compounded. If reason should grow imaginative ("Love is justice grown imaginative," declares Santayana), and make shrewd guesses about the source of evil actions, it will result in a fairer justice. But if it should become so sensitive as to recognize that the evil in the other has its source in the self or the self's society it will destroy every form of remedial justice. "Let him who is without sin cast the first stone." Thus love is both the fulfillment and the denial of remedial and punitive justice.

Love is related to distributive justice in the same manner. It is "right" that I protect my own interests as well as those of my neighbor. But an imaginative regard for the interests of my neighbor will be concerned for his needs even if they are in competition with mine. Such an imaginative concern for the neighbor's interest transcends all ordinary conceptions of equity and enjoins actions of generosity which no society can ever enjoin or regularize. But this same tendency toward the fulfillment of justice in love leads to the negation of justice by love. The neighbor's interests are avowed rather than my own and no effort is made to protect myself against the neighbor ("resist not evil"). Thus morality is fed by a realm of transcendent possibilities in which the canons of the good, established in ordinary experience, are both fulfilled and negated. That is why Jesus could symbolize the mercy of God through the impartiality of nature in which the sun shines on the evil and the good and rain falls upon the just and the unjust. The impartiality of nature is something less than human justice—and a symbol of something more, the mercy of God.

The Cross in Christian faith is the myth of the truth of the ideal of love. The Christ of Christian faith is both human and divine. His actions represent both human possibilities and the limits of human possibilities. But the possibilities which transcend the human are relevant to human experience and every moral experience suggests these ultimate possibilities. Therefore parental affection is a symbol of the love of God. ("If ye then being evil, know how to give good gifts unto your children, how much more will your heavenly Father give good gifts to them that ask him.")

The transcendent source of the meaning of life is thus in such relation to all temporal process that a profound insight into any process or reality yields a glimpse of the reality which is beyond it. This reality can be revealed and expressed only in mythical terms. These mythical terms are the most adequate symbols of reality because the reality which we experience constantly suggests a center and source of reality, which not only transcends immediate experience, but also finally transcends the rational forms and categories by which we seek to apprehend and describe it.

Sidney Hook: THE NEW FAILURE OF NERVE

IN the famous third chapter of his *Four Stages of Greek Religion* Gilbert Murray characterizes the period from 300 B.C. through the first century of the Christian era as marked by "a failure of nerve." This failure of nerve exhibited itself in "a rise of asceticism, of mysticism, in a sense, of pessimism; a loss of self confidence, of hope in this life and of faith in normal human efforts; a despair of patient inquiry, a cry for infallible revelation; an indifference to the welfare of the state, a conversion of the soul to God."

A survey of the cultural tendencies of our own times shows many signs pointing to a new failure of nerve in Western civilization. Its manifestations are more complex and sophisticated than in any previous time. It speaks in a modern idiom and employs techniques of expression and persuasion that reflect the ways of a secular culture. But at bottom

it betrays, except in one respect, the same flight from responsibility, both on the plane of action and on the plane of belief, that drove the ancient world into the shelters of pagan and Christian supernaturalism.

There is hardly a field of theoretical life from which these signs of intellectual panic, heralded as portents of spiritual revival, are lacking. No catalogue can do justice to the variety of doctrines in which this mood appears. For purposes of illustration we mention the recrudescence of beliefs in the original depravity of human nature; prophecies of doom for Western culture, no matter who wins the war or peace, dressed up as laws of social-dynamics; the frenzied search for a center of value that transcends human interests; the mystical apotheosis of "the leader" and elites; contempt for all political organizations and social programs because of the ob-

Sidney Hook, "The New Failure of Nerve," *Partisan Review*, Vol. X, No. 1, January-February 1943, pp. 2–17, 20–23. Copyright, 1943 by *Partisan Review*. Reprinted by permission.

vious failure of some of them, together with the belief that good will is sufficient to settle thorny problems of economic and social reconstruction; posturing about the cultivation of spiritual purity; the refurbishing of theological and metaphysical dogmas about the infinite as necessary presuppositions of knowledge of the finite; a concern with mystery rather than with problems, and the belief that myth and mysteries are modes of knowledge; a veritable campaign to "prove" that without a belief in God and immortality, democracy—or even plain moral decency—cannot be reasonably justified.

Liberalism—not the 19th century ideology or social theology of laissez-faire which was already moribund before the First World War—but liberalism as an intellectual temper, as faith in intelligence, as a tradition of the free market in the world of ideas is everywhere on the defensive. Before the onrush of cataclysmic social and historical changes, large sections of the intellectuals and clerics of the Western world are abandoning the hard-won critical positions of the last few centuries. In the schools, the churches, and in the literary arts, the tom-tom of theology and the bagpipes of transcendental metaphysics are growing more insistent and shrill. We are told that our children cannot be properly educated unless they are inoculated with "proper" religious beliefs; that theology and metaphysics must be given a dominant place in the curriculum of our universities; that churchmen should cultivate sacred theology before applying the social gospel; that business needs an inspired church that speaks authoritatively about absolutes,—this by the editors of *Fortune;* that what is basically at stake in this war is Christian civilization despite our gallant Chinese, Moslem, and

Russian allies; that the stability of the state depends on an *unquestioned* acceptance of a unifying dogma, sometimes identified with the hierarchical authoritarianism of Catholicism, sometimes with democracy; that none of the arts and no form of literature can achieve imaginative distinction without "postulating a transcendental reality." *Obscurantism is no longer apologetic; it has now become precious and wilful. Fundamentalism is no longer beyond the pale; it has donned a top hat and gone high church.*

Philosophy and the Assault Against Scientific Method

The primary evidence of the new failure of nerve is to be found in an attitude underlying all of the views and movements enumerated, and many others as well. It exhibits itself as a loss of confidence in scientific method, and in varied quests for a "knowledge" and "truth" which, although they give us information about the world, are uniquely different from those won by the processes of scientific inquiry. Often, with no great regard for consistency, these uniquely different truths are regarded as "superior" to the common garden variety truths of science and good sense. They are the self-proclaimed governors of the moral and theoretical economy. Their function is to point to man's natural and supernatural end and to prevent science, competent to deal only with means, from stepping out of bounds.

This distrust of scientific method is often concealed by statements to the effect that science, of course, has a certain validity in its restricted sphere and that only the pretensions of scientific philosophy, naturalism, empiricism, positivism—not to speak of materialism,—are being criticized. Yet it is not to the actual procedures of scientific inquiry that such critics go to correct this or that formulation of scientific philosophy. Instead they invoke the claims of some rival method to give us knowledge of what is beyond the competence of scientific method. Occasionally they boldly assert that their substitute method gives a more reliable and completer knowledge of the matters that the sciences report on, particularly about the behavior of man and the history of society. What an eloquent revelation is contained in Reinhold Niebuhr's words: "Science which is only science cannot be scientifically accurate." [1]

Distrust of scientific method is transformed into open hostility whenever some privileged, "private" truth pleads for exemption from the tests set up to safeguard the intelligence from illusion. The pleas for exemption take many forms. They are rarely open and direct as in the frenzy of Kierkegaard who frankly throws overboard his intelligence in order to make those leaps of despairing belief which convert his private devils into transcendent absolutes. Usually these pleas are presented as corollaries of special *theories* of knowledge, being, or experience. There are some who interpret science and discursive knowledge generally as merely a method of confirming what we *already* know in a dim but sure way by other modes of experience. If the methods of scientific inquiry do not yield this confirmation, they are held to be at fault; some other way must be found of validating and communicating primal wisdom. Others maintain that scientific method can give us only partial truths which become less partial not by subjecting them to more

[1] *The Nature and Destiny of Man*, Vol. I, p. 73, N. Y., 1941.

careful scrutiny but by incorporating them into a theological or metaphysical system whose cardinal principles are true but not testable by any method known to science. Still others openly declare it to be axiomatic that every experience, every feeling and emotion, directly reports a truth that cannot be warranted, and does not need to be warranted, by experiment or inference.

These, bluntly put, are gateways to intellectual and moral irresponsibility. They lay down roads to a happy land where we can gratify our wishes without risking a veto by stubborn fact. But of the view that every mode of experience gives direct authentic knowledge, it would be more accurate to say that it carries us far beyond the gateways. For in effect it is a defense of obscurantism. It starts from the assumption that *every* experience gives us an authentic report of the objective world instead of material for judgment. It makes our viscera an organ of knowledge. It justifies violent prejudice in its claims that if only we feel deeply enough about anything, the feeling declares some truth about the object which provokes it. This "truth" is regarded as possessing the same legitimacy as the considered judgment that finds no evidence for the feeling and uncovers its root in a personal aberration. After all is it not the case that every heresy-hunting bigot and hallucinated fanatic is convinced that there is a truth in the feelings, visions, and passions that run riot within him? Hitler is not the only one for whom questions of evidence are incidental or impertinent where his feelings are concerned. If the voice of feeling cannot be mistaken, differences would be invitations to battle, the ravings of an insane mind could legitimately claim to be prophecies of things to come. It is not only as a defense against the marginally sane that we need the safeguards of critical scientific method. Every vested interest in social life, every inequitable privilege, every "truth" promulgated as a national, class or racial truth, likewise denies the competence of scientific inquiry to evaluate its claims.

Those who hold this view sometimes seek to avoid its consequences by admitting that not every experience or feeling is as valid as every other, any more than every scientific judgment is as valid as every other. But this does not alter the logic of their position. The relative validity of different scientific judgments is established by methods of public verification open to all who submit themselves to its discipline, whereas the relative validity of feelings is decided by another private feeling.

Not infrequently the demand that the revelations of feeling, intuition or emotion about the world meet scientific canons of evidence is rejected as an arbitrary legislative decree concerning what visions are permissible and what may or may not exist. The complaint is made that such a demand impoverishes imaginative resources and blights the power to see new and fresh visions without which preoccupation with method is nothing but a word-game of sterile minds. As far as the seeing of visions and the winning of new truths are concerned, such an interpretation is nothing short of grotesque. The essential point, when the question of knowledge or truth arises, is whether we have seen a vision or been a victim of a delusion; or, to avoid the appearance of question-begging, whether we have beheld a trustworthy or untrustworthy vision. Some people claim to see what we know is not there. If seeing were believing, or if all seeing were evidence of what could be believed, independently of the conditions under which

the seeing took place, it would be easy to keep men perpetually duped.

The intelligent demand for evidence need not paralyze the pioneers of truth who catch glimpses of what until then may be undreamed of. Nor does the progress of science demand complete and exact confirmation of an hypothesis at the very outset, but only enough to institute further inquiries. The history of the sciences is sufficient evidence that the discipline of its method, far from being a bar to the discovery of new knowledge, is a positive aid in its acquisition. What other discipline can point to the acquisition of new knowledge or to truths about existence that command the universal assent of all investigators?

Nor is it true that scientific method or the philosophy of naturalism, which whole-heartedly accepts scientific method as the only reliable way of reaching truths about man, society, and nature, decrees what may or may not exist. It concerns itself only with the responsibility of the assertions that proclaim the existence of anything. It does not forbid but explores and tests. It does not jeer at the mystical swoon of dumb rapture; it denies only the mystic's retrospective cognitive claim for which no evidence is offered except the fact of a trance. It does not rule out on *a priori* grounds the existence of supernatural entities and forces. The existence of God, immortality, disembodied souls or spirits, cosmic purpose or design, as these have customarily been interpreted by the great institutional religions, are denied by naturalists for the same generic reasons that they deny the existence of fairies, elves, leprechauns, and an invisible satellite revolving between the earth and moon. There is no plausible evidence to warrant belief in them or to justify a probable inference on the basis of partial evidence.

There are other conceptions of God, to be sure, and provided they are not self-contradictory, the naturalist would be unfaithful to his own philosophy if he refused to examine the evidence for their validity. All he asks is that the conception be sufficiently determinate to make possible specific inferences of the *how, when,* and *where* of His operation. The trouble with most conceptions of God which differ from the conventional ones is that either they are so vague that no one can tell what they mean, or else they designate something in experience for which a perfectly suitable term already exists.

Unfortunately, for all their talk of appeal to experience, direct or indirect, religious experientialists dare not appeal to any experience of sufficiently determinate character to permit of definite tests. There is a certain wisdom in this reluctance. For if experience can confirm a belief, it can also disprove it. But to most supernaturalists the latter is an inadmissible possibility. We therefore find that the kind of experience to which reference is made is not only unique but uniquely self-authenticating. Those who are not blessed by these experiences are regarded as blind or deaf and, under certain circumstances, dangerous to the community. But is it not odd that those who worship Zeus on the ground of a unique experience should deny to others the right to worship Odin on the ground of a different unique experience?

Scientific method cannot deny that the secular and religious spokesmen of the supernatural hear voices, but it cannot accept these voices, as they are reported, as valid testimony about the world of fact or the world of value. It judges the truth of what is heard by what it logically leads to in the realm of empirical behavior. It seeks to draw what is reported about this world or any other into some community with the limited but precious store of responsible assertions that constitute knowledge. The attack upon scientific method, in order to be free to believe whatever voice speaks to us, is a flight from responsibility. This is the dominant characteristic of the failure of nerve.

Social Crisis and Metaphysical Hunger

The causes of the failure of nerve in our time are multiple and obvious. Economic crises, world war, a bad peace, tragically inept statesmanship, the tidal waves of totalitarianism tell the story of the twentieth century. These are the phenomena that are behind the interrupted careers, the frustrated hopes, the anxiety, the sense of being lost and alone, the growing bewilderment, fear and horror—that feed the theology of despair and the politics of wish. It is important to remember this. The "arguments" of those who have been panicked into embracing the new varieties of transcendental consolation may be met a thousand times over. But not until a democratic, freedom-and-welfare-planning economy is built out of what is left of our world, in which stable traditions can absorb the conventions of revolt of political man and the experiments of growth of individual men, will these intellectual excesses subside from epidemic to episodic proportions. Until then it is necessary to prevent intellectual hysteria from infecting those who still cling to the principles of rational experiment and analysis.

There is still another source of the new fusion of superagony and superstition. This is the inability of those liberal, labor, and socialist movements which have prided themselves on being scientific and which have lost one social campaign after another, to supply a positive philosophy, that would weld emotion and scientific intelligence, as a new rallying ground. Wilsonian idealism is dead although some do not know it, syndicalism is a fascist changeling, and orthodox Marxism is bankrupt. The grand visions of the socialist prophets have given way to petty political horse-trading and fixations on the good will of bourgeois statesmen. The left lives from day to day in a world going from worse to worse.

Into the breach has stepped the motley array of religionists filled with the *élan* of salvation and burdened with the theological baggage of centuries. *This is the one respect in which the new failure of nerve basically differs from the old.* The failure of nerve of the early Christian era sought to convert the soul to God in order to withdraw it from all concern with the world. Today the churches are so much of this world that their other worldiness is only a half-believed prophecy of man's inescapable destination rather than an ideal of personal and social life. As interpreters of divine purpose, they have now become concerned with social healing, with the institutions of society and with the bodies of men, as necessarily involved in the healing of individual souls. The world-order is to become a moral and religious order. Plans for the post-war world and for social reconstruction are coming from the Pope as well as from the humblest Protestant sect. They are now at flood-tide. The churches bid well to replace political parties as sounding boards, if not instruments, of social reform.

It is characteristic of the tendencies hostile to scientific method that they reject the view that the breakdown of capitalism and the rise of totalitarianism are primarily the result of a conjunction of material factors. Rather do they allege that the bankruptcy of Western European civilization is the direct result of the bankruptcy of the scientific and naturalistic spirit. The attempt to live by science resulted in chaos, relativism, Hitlerism and war. The latter are treated as superficial evils destined to pass like all of God's trials. But the radical evil is a scientific attitude which sacrificed true understanding for prediction and individual salvation for social control.

That science was king in the social life of the Western world, that modern ills are the consequences of our attempt to live by scientific theory and practice—these assumptions border on fantasy. No convincing evidence has ever been offered for them. On the contrary, the chief causes of our maladjustments are to be found precisely in these areas of social life *in which the rationale of scientific method has not been employed.* Where is the evidence that any Western State ever attempted to meet scientifically the challenge of poverty, unemployment, distribution of raw materials, the impact of technology? Attempts to grapple with these problems in relation to human needs in a rational and scientific spirit have run squarely against class interests and privileges which cut savagely short any inquiry into their justification. What has controlled our response to basic social problems have been principles drawn from the outworn traditions or opportunist compromises that reflect nothing but the shifting strength of the interests behind them. In either case the procedure has had little to do with the ethics and logic of scientific method. It is only by courtesy that we can call them principles at all. Drift and improvisation have been the rule. Enthusiasm for the bare *results* of the physical sciences—which undoubtedly did reach a high pitch in the 19th century—does not betoken an acceptance of a scientific or experimental philosophy of life in which all values are tested by their causes and consequences. The cry that a set of "laboratory techniques" cannot determine values in a philosophy of life betrays the literary man's illusion that the laboratory procedures of the natural sciences are the be-all and end-all of scientific method instead of restricted applications of it in special fields.

The truth is that scientific method has until now been regarded as irrelevant in testing the values embodied in social institutions. *If* one accepted the religionists' assumption that values can be grounded only on a true religion and metaphysics, together with their views about the ideal causation of events, it could be legitimately urged against them that the bankruptcy of civilization testifies to the bankruptcy of *their* metaphysics. For if science is irrelevant to values, it cannot corrupt them; and if theology and metaphysics are their sacred guardian, they are responsible for the world we live in.

Theology in a Crisis

The social principles of Christianity have had almost two thousand years in which to order the world on a moral basis. It is not likely that anything new can be discovered from its principles or that its social gospel will succeed better in eliminating war, social distress, and intense factional strife, than it did during the historical periods in which religious institutions enjoyed chief authority. And when we examine the behavior and doctrines of different religious groups as they meet the trials of our world today, the impression is reinforced that there is no more unity of purpose among them, no more agreement in program and direction of effort, than among their secular brethren. But whereas the latter *may* rely upon a method by which to limit, adjudicate and negotiate the differences among them, the former *must* absolutize their differences if they are consistent.

It is an obvious fact that all religious groups, with the exception of some Protestant churches in America, have been able to find support of their own national governments in prosecuting the war compatible with the sacred principles of Christianity. Some of them have even professed to be able to derive the necessity of such support from sacred doctrine. Cardinal Verdier of France and Cardinal Hinsley of England have declared the war to be a religious crusade; so have some of the German bishops on the other side who have blessed Hitler's arms and prayed for his victory; while the Pope himself is still neutral in respect to it. M. Maritain at the time of the Nazi-Soviet Pact declared that the war against Hitler was a just war but not a religious one. He also asserted "it is entirely understandable" that the German bishops should support their government; indeed, that it was naive to be scandalized by the divisions among religious groups on the war. Today the just war has become transformed in M. Maritain's eyes into a "religious" war. Yet no matter how they characterize the war, religious groups do not contest the validity of opposite statements made about the war by other national religious groups who take their point of departure from the *same* religious premises.

Now this is extremely odd. No one would tax theologians with insincerity. But if it is true that a religious principle or dogma is compatible with two contradictory positions in respect to the defeat of Hitlerism, then the principle or dogma in question is irrelevant to the nature of the war. And since it is true that the defeat of Hitlerism is of the very first importance for the social reconstruction of Europe, we are justified in entertaining a lively suspicion of the relevance of Christian principles to such reconstruction, if at the same time they can reconcile themselves equally well to Hitler's victory or defeat.

The only implication that can be drawn from this strange state of affairs is that religious groups are seeking, as they always have, to make of God an instrument of national policy. One of two things: Either national policy can be defended as good or just without theological sanctions or dogmas, in which case the interposition of religion obscures issues: or the defense presupposes religious dogmas, in which case, to countenance a different national policy is to betray *religious* dogma. The German bishops who admonished the Catholic soldiers in a Pastoral Letter to give their lives *"in obedience to the Fuehrer"* should have been denounced as bad Catholics. Before Catholics, Protestants and Jews urge the acceptance of their dogmas as necessary preconditions for intelligent belief in democracy and anti-Hitlerism, let them convert their own churches to democracy, and denounce religious neutrality before Hitlerism for what it is, connivance with the enemy. This is their sector of the battle. But, better still, let them take their theology out of politics.

On the very question of the war itself the Protestant churches of America are split wide open although this is somewhat concealed by the unanimity of interest in problems of post-war reconstruction. Yet no matter with what voice the churches speak on the issues of the day, they do so not as other associations of citizens who must face demands of empirical evidence, but as guardians of a revelation which gives them unique knowledge of man and his destiny.

Religion can escape showing its credentials concerning the inspiration of its knowledge but not concerning its validity. For the reliability of any knowledge is tested in the necessities of intelligent action. That test, together with the varying counsel of the churches on specific social policies, is sufficient to indicate that there is no unique religious knowledge or religious guidance. When Church pronouncements about the nature of the world are not irrelevant or clearly false, they can be more plausibly derived from positions that churches usually characterize as unbelieving. When the claims to unique knowledge are exploded, the last resort of religionists is the assertion that religious beliefs, and only religious beliefs, can supply that dynamic faith without which secular defence of the good society is ineffectual, unable to implement its own humanist ideals.

Faith, Sin, and Good Sense

The defense of religious faith takes many forms. Most of them are variations on the theme that if the beliefs of faith were false, the world would be a terrible place: therefore they must be true. Or since the beliefs of faith are consoling, they cannot be false. Sometimes the argument rises a little higher. Because not everything can be proved, since even science must make assumptions, some faith in something is unavoidable if one is to believe or do anything. Therefore faith in the absurd is justifiable. But only our faith, not the other fellow's! On its most sophisticated level, faith is defended not as a specific belief but as an attitude of wisdom and resignation towards the human situation. When it is realized that such faith is not distinctively religious at all, either there is a relapse into metaphysical double-talk about faith also being a form of knowledge, or religion is defined so that all people who have faith or passion, i.e., who are not yet dead, are regarded as religious and committed to religious beliefs. But when religious belief is a universal coefficient of all other beliefs, it is irrelevant to them. This may be seen most clearly in the theology of Reinhold Niebuhr.

Reinhold Niebuhr is one of those men of whom Emerson said they were better than their theology. A radical honest intelligence, he brings to bear upon specific problems of social change a scientific attitude and rare courage that make his discussions always illuminating. But not a single one of the positions that Niebuhr takes on the momentous issues of social and political life is dependent on his theology. One may accept his rather reactionary theology, which is an eloquent combination of profound disillusionment in human action and a violent belief in human ideals, and deny all his secular views. Or one may accept the latter, as so many of his friends do, and regard the former as moving rhetoric that breathes passionate conviction about something whose very sense is in doubt. Indeed, if we look closely at Niebuhr's theology, and take it out of the language of myth and paradox, we find that whatever is acceptable in it to critical thought is an obscure retelling of what was known to the wiser unbelievers of the past.

Consider, for example, Niebuhr's conception of religion. It is "the primary and ultimate act of faith by which life is endowed with meaning. Without that act of faith life cannot be lived at all." [2] To be alive is to be religious, and the atheists, the irreligious, the agnostics, have been converted by definition: they all have religion. This is innocent enough so long as we never lose sight of the differences between religions or *what* men believe in, and so long as we realize that although life cannot be lived without some acts of faith, death may be the consequence of other acts of faith, e.g., faith that pneumonia can be cured by absent treatment. What Niebuhr must now show as a theologian is that the faith necessary for life is necessarily faith in God. This he completely fails to do. Instead by another essay in redefinition—one not so innocent—he equates the meaning which is the object or reference of *any* faith with God. "There is no action without religious orientation and no religion without God." [3] To be alive is not only to be religious, it is to have faith in God even if we deny his existence. This is still not the end. Niebuhr must now as a *Christian* theologian show that the God we affirm in action is the God of revealed Christianity who is transcendent to the world and yet intimately connected with it. This is accomplished in his Gifford Lectures by describing man as a "self-transcendent spirit" consumed by a metaphysical anxiety and hunger which can only be appeased by belief in the symbolical (not literal!) truth of the Incarnation. Insofar as arguments are employed instead of exhortation they are fallacious. For example: what is unique about the human spirit cannot be derived from man's animal

[2] *Modern Monthly*, Vol. 8, p. 712.
[3] "Religion and Action," *Religion in the Modern World*, University of Pennsylvania Bicentennial Conference (1941) p. 91.

nature; nor is it an expression of reason. Therefore, infers Niebuhr, man is a child of God who can only comprehend himself "by a principle of comprehension which is beyond his comprehension." One mystery calls for another and the plain fact that what is distinctive about human traits has its origin and fruit in the social and cultural matrix is not so much as considered.

Man, Niebuhr asserts, is not only a creature of God, he is a sinner. He is an inevitable sinner and yet cannot escape responsibility for his sins. He is a sinner because he forgets that he is a creature of God, because he thinks he is more than he is, knows more than he does, because, in short, he is not God. When he is contritely aware of his sinfulness, of its inevitability and his responsibility for it, grace descends upon his soul and he receives remission from sin.

There is a simple moral homily that can be tortured out of this oxymoronic language but it is completely spoiled by Niebuhr's theology.

What Niebuhr is telling us is that every effort, every movement of man in warding off evil or achieving good, leads him to "the sin of imperialism in action." Whether we are selfish or righteous, the tincture of sin is present. For we absolutize the relative, dogmatize insight, eternalize the fleeting, take the part for the whole. Man deludes himself into believing that he sees the infinite from a finite perspective, and that he transcends self-interest and selfishness in his conceptions of impartial justice. All of his ideals, including his God, he makes in his own image. In his struggle to achieve his limited ideals as if they were absolute, he consequently is guilty of fanaticism whose evils may be not less than those he set out to rectify. Man must therefore accept some supernatural

standard to curb the conflicts of partial truths, each claiming to be the whole truth.

What is here correctly perceived as a problem still remains a problem, for Niebuhr's solution is stultifying. The conflict of absolutes is to be settled by appeal to another absolute which on Niebuhr's own theology is necessarily injected with human finitude! This is a romantic and violent solution of a human predicament already violently distorted to begin with. Niebuhr writes as if all men were naturally romantic theologians, victims of a fantastic logic according to which, if God did not exist, *they* must be God. He ignores the entire tradition of scientific and naturalistic philosophy that has never claimed divinity for man nor infallibility for his judgment. The doctrine of original sin turns out to be nothing more than the discovery that man is a limited creature. But this is no more justification for believing he is essentially evil than that he is essentially good. For these are qualities that depend upon the use man makes of his limitations. Naturalist philosophers have urged men to understand the causes of their limitations, so that by reducing the margins of ignorance and increasing their scientific knowledge, they may be less limited. The whole enterprise of scientific method with its self-corrective procedures cuts under the dogmatism, absolutism and fanaticism of Niebuhr's theological man at the same time as it gives us conclusions that are sufficiently reliable to overcome some specific limitations. Niebuhr would frighten men out of their mistaken belief in omnipotence by a fairy tale about a creature that is absolutely omnipotent. The humility it induces is one of fear, not the humility which is fostered by knowledge of human limitations and ignorance. His wisdom does not carry further than the caution that no claim is completely justified, but he is helpless before the problem of determining the degree and extent of its justification, so necessary in order to get on with the problems in hand. Whenever Niebuhr tackles these problems, he deserts his theology.

It is true that intellectual pride is an expression of "original sin" insofar as we make a claim to know what we do not know and overlook the natural and historical origins of reason. Niebuhr is very eloquent about the dangers of intellectual pride. "Fanaticism is always a partly conscious, partly unconscious attempt to hide the fact of ignorance and to obscure the problem of skepticism." And again: "The real fact is that all the pretensions of final knowledge and ultimate truth are partly prompted by the uneasy feeling that the truth is not final and also by an uneasy conscience which realizes that the interests of the ego are compounded with this truth." [4] True, but Niebuhr should address these words not to naturalists but to theologians, for in the history of thought it has been the naturalists who have exposed the pretensions of final truths and who have uncovered the nerve of interest behind the absolute values of church, state, and conscience. Science has known its dogmatism, too. But the cure of bad science is better science, not theology.

On many specific issues of scientific inquiry Niebuhr is one with us. Despite his extravagant rhetoric, he does not believe in blowing out the candle-light of intelligence and wallowing in the dark night of the soul in an effort to make mysteries more mysterious. The only point at which Niebuhr seems to use his theology is in situations where values and partial interests are locked in mortal combat.

But does an appeal to the absolute really help us here? Is any war so fanatical and bestial as a religious war in which the conditioned values of social and personal interests take on the awful authority of unconditioned claims? Is might right when it is divine might? Is not the God of faith always the God of limited, erring and partial men? If we must have an absolute, let us look for it elsewhere. Against Niebuhr's myth of a private and mysterious absolute, we counterpose the public and self-critical absolute of scientific method. By evaluating claims in the light of their causes and consequences, it makes clear the interests from which they spring, and the meaning of what they propose. By guiding us to the construction of a social order whose institutions provide for the negotiation and compromise of claims on the basis of the completest knowledge available, it promises not absolute security but greater security. It does not pretend to make men gods but to treat more intelligently the problem always at hand. It is not incompatible with action, even with revolutionary action on a large scale. Nothing is won forever but something is always won. How to get men to accept this absolute method—and to test it by its fruits, not only in the realm of nature but of human affairs—is a specific problem of scientific politics and education concerning which theology can tell us nothing. [5]

Democracy and the Hebraic-Christian Tradition

These new currents of Protestantism which profess sincere acceptance of pres-

[4] *The Nature and Destiny of Man*, p. 196.

[5] For a more extended critique of Niebuhr, cf. my "Social Change and Original Sin," *New Leader*, Nov. 11, 1941.

ent-day democracy employ arguments whose force is drawn from a key assumption. It asserts that modern democracy has been derived from, and can only be justified by, the theological dogmas of Hebraic-Christianity according to which all men are created by God and equal before Him. This assumption is the common ground of unity of all religious and metaphysical rationalizations of democracy. It is the rallying point of the much publicized Conference on Science, Philosophy and Religion in their Relation to the Democratic Way of Life, whose pronouncements indicate that it has officially accepted Maritain's Catholic conception of a pluralistic, hierarchically organized culture, crowned by religion, as "the cornerstone on which human civilization must be erected in our day." Scientific inquiry has a place in it: it will meet the "need for men to attain that increased measure of knowledge which, according to Francis Bacon, brings men back to God." This Hebraic-Christian philosophy of democracy and culture is presented to a world in which a false conception of scientific knowledge has made it "peculiarly resistant to the teachings of religion. . . ." [6]

It can be briefly demonstrated that the derivation of modern democracy from the dogma that all men are created by God and equal before Him is (1) logically invalid (2) historically false and (3) irrelevant to the pressing problem of democratic defense and reconstruction.

(1) From the alleged fact that all men are equal before God, it does not at all follow logically that they are, or should be, equal before the state or enjoy equal rights in the community. This must be

[6] All quotations from the official statement of the Third Annual Conference, New York *Times*, September 1, 1942.

justified by other considerations. Even on the theological scheme, although God is equally the creator of angels, men, animals and things, they are not all equal in value before Him. Men are also equal before death, pain, disease and the tax-collector. But how they should be treated often depends upon their relative state of health, their efforts, the consequences of their efforts, and other *differential* features of their behavior. Some Christians have held—with as much logic as their brethren who drew contrary conclusions —that because all men are equally sinners in the sight of the Lord, their social and political inequalities in this transitory life are unimportant. Not infrequently, pious Christians have believed that these inequalities are our punishment for the sins of our fathers. If men have a common origin, biological or theological, that in itself is not logically sufficient for asserting that they must or should have common opportunities or common education or common citizenship. If we believe that they should have, as we do, then we believe it on grounds whose validity would be unaffected whether they had a common origin or not.

Nor is the alleged fact that man was created by God a logical ground for honoring Him. We are told both by the Pope and the Archbishop of Canterbury and the American Institute of Judaism that the dignity of man lies not in himself but in that he is a child of God. In the course of a typical Catholic denunciation of "atheistic saboteurs" who would keep the idea of God separate from our government, Professor Manion of Notre Dame, at a public meeting sponsored by the Conference, proclaims: "The only reason why we have to respect this so-called dignity of man is because it is God-created." [7] The logic would be just

[7] Proceedings of Third Conference, p. 538.

as bad even if the rhetoric were better. As well say that the only reason we have for not lying is that it is forbidden by God. Or that the only reason for appreciating the beauty of a landscape is that it is God's handiwork. The origin of a thing may have a bearing upon its nature. But the value of a thing cannot be inferred from its origin. It is not putative original nature but what emerges in the course of developing nature which is relevant to normative judgment. To judge people not by their origins, for which they are not responsible, but by their efforts, fruits, and achievements is a sound democratic maxim.[8]

(2) There is little warrant for the view that the theological dogmas of Hebraic-Christianity are the historical source of modern democracy. Judaism countenanced slavery while Christianity never condemned it in principle. The Church was one of the mainstays of feudalism; until its real-estate holdings were raided by absolute monarchs, it furnished the chief theoretical justification of the divine right of kings. Ideologically, modern democratic theory owes more to Stoic philosophy and Roman law than to Christian dogma.

Religious institutions based on supernatural dogmas tend towards theocracy. Priesthoods have often been hereditary, and when not tightly closed corporations, rarely subject to democratic influences. It has sometimes been urged as a mitigating feature of the hierarchical, authoritarian structure of the Church that "a peasant might become a Pope." True, but so can an Austrian housepainter or the son of a Georgian cobbler become a

dictator. Does that alter the character of totalitarianism?

(3) We are asked to accept religious dogmas as true mainly on the grounds of their effectiveness in combating Hitlerism. This in turn rests, as we have seen, upon the notion that Fascism is the consequence not of economic conditions, nationalist tradition, and disastrous political policies inside Germany and out, but of the spread of positivism, secularism, and humanism. Why Fascism should then have arisen in such strongly religious and metaphysical countries as Italy and Germany and not in such scandalously heretical and positivistic countries as England and America, is something that the neo-Thomists, and their fellow-travellers do not explain.

None of the specific proposals of social reform that issue from religious conclaves, or even the principles sometimes offered to justify them, follow from the theological dogmas that preface their announcement. This is no more surprising than the absence of connection between the pleas for divine guidance which since the war stud the speeches of *all* statesmen of belligerent countries, except those of Stalin,[9] and the content of the speeches. Specific proposals to insure peace, security and freedom warrant attentive consideration no matter from what quarter they come. But their value in effecting what they claim to accomplish depends not on pious faith and good will but upon their consequences which can be adequately explored only by rigorous scientific thought without benefit of theology. To the extent that the scope of scientific thinking is restricted or limited to judgments of bare

[8] For a more detailed refutation of the attempts to ground democracy upon theological and metaphysical foundations, cf. "The Philosophical Presuppositions of Democracy," *Ethics,* April, 1942, pp. 275–296.

[9] For Stalin the dialectic takes the place of Providence. And since June 22nd, 1941, the Soviet radio has discovered that Nazism is a movement which seeks to destroy Christianity.

fact, the new social consciousness of the Christian churches will have just as little relevance to the future as their old consolatory ideals to the past. At best it will take flight from power politics; at worst it will act as a cover for it.

* * *

The new failure of nerve in contemporary culture is compounded of unwarranted hopes and unfounded beliefs. It is a desperate quest for a quick and all-inclusive faith that will save us from the trouble of thinking about difficult problems. These hopes, beliefs, and faiths pretend to a knowledge which is not knowledge and to a superior insight not responsible to the checks of intelligence. The more fervently they are held the more complete will be their failure. Out of them will grow a disillusion in the possibility of intelligent human effort so profound that even if Hitler is defeated, the blight of Hitlerism may rot the culture of his enemies.

Suggestions for Additional Reading

For the general intellectual history of the period from the Civil War to the present see Merle Curti, *The Growth of American Thought* (New York, 1943) and Henry S. Commager, *The American Mind: An Interpretation of American Thought and Character Since the 1880's* (New Haven, 1950). A history of religion covering the period is Winfred E. Garrison, *The March of Faith: The Story of Religion in America Since 1865* (New York, 1933). Briefer accounts will be found in W.W. Sweet, *The Story of Religions in America* (New York, 1950) and J. C. Brauer, *Protestantism in America: A Narrative History* (Philadelphia, 1953). Herbert W. Schneider, *Religion in Twentieth Century America* (Cambridge, 1952) is a systematic review of developments during the latter half of this period.

For an interesting description of the state of religion in the 80's see the two chapters, "The Churches and the Clergy" and "The Influence of Religion" in James Bryce, *The American Commonwealth*, 2 vols. (New York, 1891—second edition revised). This characterization should be compared with that of the recent past and the present by Harold Laski in his chapter, "Religion in America," *The American Democracy: A Commentary and Interpretation* (New York, 1948) and with the descriptions of religious beliefs and observances in a fairly typical American community by Robert S. Lynd and Helen M. Lynd in *Middletown: A Study in Contemporary American Culture* (New York, 1929) and *Middletown in Transition: A Study in Cultural Conflicts* (New York, 1937). Reinhold Niebuhr has briefly stated his conception of the present situation in an article, "The Impact of Protestantism Today," *Atlantic Monthly*, 181 (Feb., 1948), 57–62.

An excellent brief account of the development of the theory of evolution by Lyell, Darwin, and their predecessors is John W. Judd, *The Coming of Evolution: The Story of a Great Scientific Revolution* (Cambridge, England, 1910). For an authoritative and highly readable statement of the theory as it stands today see George G. Simpson, *The Meaning of Evolution* (New Haven, 1949—reprinted in abridged form by Mentor Books, New York, 1951).

Two classic accounts of the age-old debate over the relation of science to religion are John W. Draper, *History of the Conflict Between Religion and Science* (New York, 1874) and Andrew D. White, *A His-*

tory of the Warfare of Science with Theology in Christendom (New York, 1896). Detailed treatments of the influence of evolutionary theories upon American thought are: Edward A. White, Science and Religion in American Thought: The Impact of Naturalism (Palo Alto, 1952) and a volume of essays by various authors edited by Stow Persons, Evolutionary Thought in America (New Haven, 1950). Richard Hofstadter, Social Darwinism in American Thought 1860–1915 (Philadelphia, 1944—revised edition, Boston, 1955) is the most adequate treatment of the influence of Spencer and Darwin on social theory. Dirk J. Struik, Yankee Science in the Making (Boston, 1948) has a chapter on the early reactions of American scientists to the theories of Lyell and Darwin. For the effects of the theory of evolution in philosophy and theology see Herbert W. Schneider, A History of American Philosophy (New York, 1946), Ch. VI, "Evolution and Human Progress." This book also contains a particularly useful guide to the literature of the subject. Philip P. Wiener, Evolution and the Founders of Pragmatism (Cambridge, 1949), shows in detail the connection between the theory and an indigenous American philosophy. F. H. Foster, The Modern Movement in American Theology (New York, 1939) is a penetrating discussion of the development of theological thought from the middle of the nineteenth century up to the first decade of the twentieth.

In addition to these books there are a number of valuable articles dealing with the influence of evolution. Of these the most profound is the title essay of John Dewey's The Influence of Darwin on Philosophy and Other Essays in Contemporary Thought (New York, 1910). Conrad Wright, "The Religion of Geology," New England Quarterly, 14 (1941), 335–358, discusses the attempts to reconcile Genesis with science. Bert J. Loewenberg has written three articles: "Darwinism Comes to America: 1859–1900," Mississippi Valley Historical Review, 28 (1941), 339–368; "The Controversy over Evolution in New England;

1859–1873," New England Quarterly, 8 (1935), 232–257; and "The Reaction of American Scientists to Darwinism," American Historical Review, 38 (1932–33), 687–701. Other useful articles are: Sidney Ratner, "Evolution and the Rise of the Scientific Spirit in America," Philosophy of Science, 3 (1936), 104–122; Herbert W. Schneider, "The Influence of Darwin and Spencer on American Philosophical Theology," Journal of the History of Ideas, 6 (1945), 3–18; Max H. Fisch, "Evolution in American Philosophy," Philosophical Review, 56 (1947), 357–373.

An excellent brief exposition of more recent developments of religious thought is George F. Thomas, "New Forms for Old Faith," published in a volume entitled Changing Patterns in American Civilization (Philadelphia, 1949). Some of the books dealing in more detail with this subject are: Edwin E. Aubrey, Present Theological Tendencies (New York, 1936); Arnold S. Nash, Editor, Protestant Thought in the Twentieth Century (New York, 1951); Gerald B. Smith, Current Christian Thinking (Chicago, 1928). The effect of world war and depression upon many leading protestant thinkers is well illustrated by two series of articles in the Christian Century—the first in the issues published during 1939, the second in 1949—under the general title, "How My Mind Has Changed in This Decade." Another interesting symposium appeared in the numbers of the Partisan Review for 1950 under the title, "Religion and the Intellectuals."

The literature of the controversy over Darwinism is huge and only a representative list of typical and important contributions to it can here be given. The leading scientific proponent of Darwin in America was Asa Gray. His reviews and articles have been collected in Darwiniana (New York, 1884). Louis Agassiz was the leader of the opposition. A brief statement of his argument is "Evolution and Permanence of Type," Atlantic Monthly, 33 (1874), 92–101. The most powerful early defense of Darwin on both scientific and philosophical grounds was made by Chauncey Wright. His reviews and papers have been reprinted in *Philosophical Discussions* (New York, 1877). John Fiske, an ardent disciple of Herbert Spencer, defended the theory in numerous articles and books. His major contribution, *Outlines of Cosmic Philosophy Based on the Doctrine of Evolution* (Boston, 1874), attracted wide attention and exerted great influence.

Typical of the theological opposition to Darwinism is Charles Hodge, *What is Darwinism?* (New York, 1874). (For a good review of the prolific literature of this sort see Loewenberg's article, "The Controversy Over Evolution in New England," referred to above.) Numerous counterattempts to "reconcile" evolution with religion were made by scientists, by philosophers, and by theologians. In general, these works attempt to equate the evolutionary process with divine creation on the "installment plan." Examples of this literature by scientists are the botanist Asa Gray's *Natural Science and Religion* (New York, 1880) and the geologist Joseph Le Conte's *Evolution, Its Nature, Its Evidences, and Its Relation to Religious Thought* (New York, 1888). Three little books by John Fiske, *The Destiny of Man* (Boston, 1884), *The Idea of God as Affected by Modern Knowledge* (Boston, 1891) and *Through Nature to God* (Boston, 1899), exemplify the philosophical approach. Typical works by leading clergymen are Henry Ward Beecher, *Evolution and Religion* (New York, 1885), James McCosh, *The Religious Aspects of Evolution* (New York, 1888) and Lyman Abbott, *The Theology of An Evolutionist* (Boston, 1897). The most influential and persuasive of the "free thinkers," who denied religion in the name of science, was Robert Ingersoll. A good summary of his argument is the lecture, "Why I am an Agnostic," in *The Works of Robert G. Ingersoll*, IV, 5–67 (New York, 1906). For a detailed account of the various groups of free thinkers see Sidney Warren, *American Freethought, 1860–1914* (New York, 1943). Among more recent contributions

by scientists are Henry N. Russell, *Fate and Freedom* (New Haven, 1927) and R. A. Millikan, *Evolution in Science and Religion* (New Haven, 1927)—both attempts at reconciliation. L. T. More, *The Dogma of Evolution* (Princeton, 1925) is a hostile criticism of some regnant theories of evolution by a physicist. Typical of the efforts by philosophers and theologians to achieve a synthesis are: F. H. Johnson, *God in Evolution: A Pragmatic Study of Theology* (New York, 1911); Edmund Noble, *Purposive Evolution: The Link Between Science and Religion* (New York, 1926); W. M. Horton, *Theism and the Scientific Spirit* (New York, 1933); W. E. Hocking, *Science and the Idea of God* (Chapel Hill, 1944).

The only adequate study of the great fundamentalist revival after World War I is Norman F. Furniss, *The Fundamentalist Controversy, 1918–1931* (New Haven, 1954). S. G. Cole, *The History of Fundamentalism* (New York, 1931) is a competent but pedestrian work which deals primarily with the struggle for control within the protestant denominations and neglects the controversy over evolution. There are two chapters on fundamentalism in Virginius Dabney, *Liberalism in the South* (Chapel Hill, 1932). Other brief discussions are: Harbor Allen, "The Anti-Evolution Campaign in America," *Current History*, 24 (1926), 893–897 and E. Mims, "Why the South is Anti-Evolution," *Worlds Work*, 50 (1925), 548–552. The survey reported by J. H. Leuba in *The Belief in God and Immortality* (Boston, 1916) provided fundamentalists with much of their evidence for the charge that colleges and universities were undermining the faith of students.

E. C. Vanderlaan has compiled an excellent selection from the literature of the controversy, *Fundamentalism vs. Modernism* (New York, 1925). The basic tenets of the fundamentalists were set forth in *The Fundamentals: A Testimony* (12 vols., Chicago, 1910–1912)—a series of pamphlets which were sent out to all protestant ministers in the English-speaking world. A brief statement of their position by one of the leaders of the movement is W. B. Riley, "The Faith of the Fundamentalists," *Current History*, 26 (1927), 434–440. See also his *Inspiration or Evolution* (Cleveland, 1926). William Jennings Bryan's most detailed and systematic exposition of his views is *In His Image* (New York, 1922). More authoritative is the defense of fundamentalism by a competent biblical scholar, J. Gresham Machen, in *Christianity and Liberalism* (New York, 1924).

The fullest account of the Scopes trial is *Bryan and Darrow at Dayton* (New York, 1925) compiled by Leslie H. Allen from the court record and various statements issued at the time. The final speech which Bryan prepared but was not able to deliver at the trial is reprinted here and also in W. J. Bryan and Mary B. Bryan, *The Memoirs of William Jennings Bryan* (Philadelphia, 1925). There are brief accounts in Irving Fine, *Clarence Darrow for the Defence* (New York, 1941), and Paxton Hibben, *The Peerless Leader: William Jennings Bryan* (New York, 1929). The play by Jerome Lawrence and Robert E. Lee, *Inherit the Wind* (New York, 1955), successfully recaptures the tense excitement of that dramatic event, and T. S. Stribling's novel, *Teeftallow* (New York, 1926), gives a vivid characterization of the hill folk who supported the legislation in Tennessee.

Commentators and critics, of course, were legion. Among the replies to the fundamentalists' attack on science were Henry Fairfield Osborn, *Evolution and Religion in Education: Polemics of the Fundamentalist Controversy of 1922–1926* (New York, 1926) and Maynard Shipley, *The War on Modern Science: A Short History of the Fundamentalist Attacks on Evolution and Modernism* (New York, 1927). For H. L. Mencken's mordant characterization see "In Memoriam: W. J. B.," "The Hills of Zion," and "Protestantism in the Republic," in *Prejudices: Fifth Series* (New York, 1926). Harold K. Beale has a chapter, "Freedom of Expression: Science" in his *Are American Teachers Free?* (New York,

1936) in which he reviews the legislative and other more informal restraints applied in many states. Walter Lippmann, *American Inquisitors: A Commentary on Dayton and Chicago* (New York, 1928), from which excerpts are included in these readings, is the best discussion of the important political problem of control of the public schools—the real legal question involved in the trial.

Representatives of the modernist position in more recent times are: Shailer Mathews, *The Faith of Modernism* (New York, 1925); John Moffatt Mecklin, *The Survival Value of Christianity* (New York, 1926); and Harry Emerson Fosdick, *As I See Religion* (New York, 1932). An interesting indication of waning confidence among the modernists during the depression years is Fosdick's "Beyond Modernism—A Sermon," *The Christian Century*, 52 (1935), 1549–1552.

John Dewey's *A Common Faith* (New Haven, 1934)—the first chapter of which is included in these readings—is the best statement of humanism. Also excellent is Walter Lippmann's *Preface to Morals* (New York, 1935). Among other expositions are: Charles Francis Potter, *Humanizing Religion* (New York, 1933) and Corliss Lamont, *Humanism as a Philosophy* (New York, 1949). Typical criticism of the humanist position by a modernist is Harry Emerson Fosdick's "Religion Without God? —The Limitations of Humanism," originally published in *Harper's Magazine* and reprinted in *As I See Religion*. To this Elmer Davis replied under the title, "God Without Religion," *Harper's*, 160 (1929–30), 397–409. A volume of essays edited by Henry Van Deusen, *The Christian Answer* (New York, 1946) is an attempt by a theologically more conservative group to meet the arguments of agnostics and humanists. Some articles in which naturalists take the offensive against their critics are: John Dewey, "Anti-Naturalism in Extremis," *Partisan Review*, 10 (1943), 24–39; Ernest Nagel, "Malicious Philosophies of Science," *Partisan Review*, 10 (1943), 40–57; Herbert Feigl, "Naturalism and Humanism," *The American Quarterly*, 1 (1949), 135–148; and Sidney Hook, "Intelligence and Evil in Human History," in *Freedom and Experience: Essays Presented to Horace M. Kallen* (Ithaca, 1947).

Reinhold Niebuhr's most complete exposition of his version of the new orthodoxy is *The Nature and Destiny of Man* (2 vols., New York, 1941 & 1943). Perhaps best among his many books for a briefer presentation of his position as a whole is *Faith and History* (New York, 1949). His paper, "The Truth in Myths"—included in these readings—was criticized by D. C. Macintosh in an article entitled, "Is Theology Reducible to Mythology?" *The Review of Religion*, 4 (1939–40), 140–158. Niebuhr's reply and a rejoinder by Macintosh are in the same volume, pp. 304–308 and 434–437. A symposium of critical essays by various authors on Niebuhr, edited by Charles W. Kegley and Robert W. Bretall, is *Reinhold Niebuhr: His Religious, Social, and Political Thought* (New York, 1956). This book also contains a brief intellectual autobiography, Niebuhr's replies to his critics, and a bibliography of his writings. Perhaps the best introduction to the theology of Paul Tillich, an equally influential proponent of the new orthodoxy, is *Biblical Religion and the Search for Ultimate Reality* (Chicago, 1935). For criticism of the new orthodoxy by a group of modernists and humanists see H. N. Wieman, et al., *Religious Liberals Reply* (Boston, 1947). Of particular interest in this volume is the trenchant analysis of Niebuhr's position by Arthur E. Murphy en-

titled "Coming to Grips With the Nature and Destiny of Man."

Catholics participated in this controversy only during its early stages, while the position of the Church was still undefined. Since Catholic theologians distinguish between the divine inspiration and a literal interpretation of the Bible, they are able to accept a theistic version of evolution. For brief statements of this view see the article "Evolution" in *A Catholic Dictionary* (New York, 1949) and the *Catholic Encyclopaedia*. More detailed treatments of the question by Catholic writers are: J. A. O'Brien, *Evolution and Religion* (New York, 1932); William M. Agar, *Catholicism and the Progress of Science* (New York, 1940); Henri de Dorlodot, *Darwinism and Catholic Thought* (New York, 1922).

The best way of realizing the emotional as well as the intellectual impact of the radical shift in the climate of opinion effected by the theory of evolution is to read biographies of men who lived through that period. Some of these are: Henry Adams, *The Education of Henry Adams* (Boston, 1918); Lyman Abbott, *Reminiscences* (Boston, 1915); Paxton Hibben, *Henry Ward Beecher: An American Portrait* (New York, 1927); J. S. Clark, *The Life and Letters of John Fiske* (2 vols., Boston, 1917); Clarence H. Cramer, *Royal Bob: The Life of Robert G. Ingersoll* (Indianapolis, 1952); John F. Mecklin, *My Quest for Freedom* (New York, 1945); Gamaliel Bradford, *D. L. Moody—A Worker in Souls* (New York, 1928); W. J. Tucker, *My Generation* (Boston, 1919); Andrew D. White, *Autobiography* (New York, 1905).